Introduction to Business Economics Workbook

Tony Shafto

Prepared in association with
the Coventry Business School

Stanley Thornes (Publishers) Ltd

Text and original line illustrations © Tony Shafto 1991

First published in 1991 by:
Stanley Thornes (Publishers) Ltd
Old Station Drive
Leckhampton
CHELTENHAM GL53 0DN
England

British Library Cataloguing in Publication Data

Shafto, Tony
    Introduction to Business Economics Workbook
    1. Title
    338.7

    ISBN 0-7487-1359-x

Typeset by the Teaching Resources Unit, Coventry Polytechnic, Coventry.
Printed in Great Britain by Scotprint Ltd, Musselburgh

Contents _____

Preface _____

Introduction to Business Economics Workbook was produced to supplement and accompany Introduction to Business Economics by John Old and Tony Shafto to provide the core texts for a comprehensive teaching package for first year students on a wide range of economics, business studies engineering and technical courses at the Coventry Polytechnic.

These texts aim to meet the growing need for soundly based, practical material to introduce students to the foundations of economic analysis and its practical applications and relevance to business practice. The author believes in the importance of educating future business specialists of all kinds to the realities of the business organisation as an economic structure operating in a competitive market environment but conforming also to the ethical and social expectations of a modern civilised society. In this society the State inevitably has a major role and business managers at every level have to be aware of the various ways their work is likely to be affected by government policies and actions.

It is hoped that this workbook will assist lecturers to cope with the pressures of large, mixed courses but at the same time encourage teaching methods that depend less on a one way flow of information from the teacher to the taught and more on a shared exploration of the modern economic and business environment in which self study, student enquiry and research and structured discussion play a greater part than the traditional lecture.

I would like to thank the management of the Coventry Business School for affording the time and facilities to prepare this workbook, Bill Boswell of the Teaching Resources Unit of Coventry Polytechnic for his very great skills and patience and Brian Carvell, College and Overseas director of Stanley Thornes.

Tony Shafto, Coventry Business School 1991

1

An economic framework

Topic summary

Essential concepts

Economics is the study of the way people use the resources available to them to maintain and develop their living standards. This has some important implications.

Wants

Communities of people tend to have unlimited desires. These go beyond biological needs and the requirements for survival. The economist does not attempt to judge the worthiness of wants. If they exist, the economist's function is to measure them and calculate their implications for resource use.

Production

This is the process of seeking to satisfy wants. Any activity of this kind is included in the economic term **production** but in the business organisation the word is more commonly used to distinguish the effort of making a good or carrying out a service from the associated **commercial** activities of distribution, marketing and finance.

Resources and the factors of production

The resources needed for production are normally classified as:

- **Land**
  This is the **space** required to do anything and **raw materials** or **basic (primary) resources** extracted from nature.

- **Labour**
  The mental and physical effort engaged in production.

- **Capital**
  This includes **physical capital**, equipment, machinery etc. and **financial capital**, the purchasing power required to acquire physical capital.

1

Scarcity

Resources are said to be **scarce** not just in the sense that they are in limited supply, although many are, but also in the sense that if a resource is used for one purpose it cannot at the same time be used for another.

Opportunity cost and resource cost

Almost all resources can only be used at a **cost** measured in relation to the lost opportunity of using them for some other productive activity. This is called **opportunity cost** and it is measured in terms of the next preferred activity that has been sacrificed in favour of the one actually chosen. Activities also involve a **resource cost** which is measured in terms of the resources they use.

The economic problem

Since people are constantly seeking to satisfy unlimited wants from scarce resources they must constantly make choices about the use of these resources. Choice is **rational** if it is based on a comparison of cost and benefit obtained from the use, and if it is consistent, i.e. if A is preferred to B, and B preferred to C, then for rational consistency A must be preferred to C.

The economic questions

These are the basis for every production decision. They ask:

- **What** is to be produced?
- **How** is it to be produced?
- **For whom** is it to be produced?

The decision-making process, i.e. who decides the answers to these questions and how decisions are arrived at, is essentially political, involving an examination of the decision-making structures within the economy. It is difficult, therefore, to separate economics from politics and most early economists regarded themselves as students of the **political economy**.

The range of economics

For many years economics has been studied on two planes. **Microeconomics** has involved the study of the firm, the industry and particular product markets. **Macroeconomics** has involved the study of the general economic forces operating within the community as a whole; the community itself is considered at the various levels of the nation, the economic region, e.g. the European Community, and the world market. This separation derives from the belief that certain economic trends or forces take on different characteristics when operating at the community level than when operating at the individual level. The whole is more than just the sum of the parts. More recently there has been a tendency to relate the two areas of study much more closely together and to study both the macro consequences of decisions taken at the micro level and to examine the micro implications of macroeconomic policies. **Business Economics** attempts to examine **all** the forces, both micro and macro which have a bearing on decision making within the business organisation.

Techniques

Economic models

The term model is used in the social sciences to indicate a simplified version of an aspect of the real world. Its purpose is to aid understanding of the forces at work and to enable predictions to be made of the effect of these forces and of changes in them. The simpler the model and the fewer the forces or **variables** taken into account, the easier it is to understand but the further it will be from reality. The closer the model is to reality the more complex it becomes and the greater the risk that it will fail to achieve its basic purpose. There has to be a balance between simplicity and reality taking into account the model's purpose. For introductory studies simplicity is favoured.

Predictions

The actions of individuals are, to a large extent, unpredictable. No one would attempt to forecast what each individual customer entering a supermarket was likely to buy but the actions of large groups are highly predictable if enough is known about the forces affecting their decisions. Store managers can make reasonably accurate predictions of sales of their goods in relation to, say, each 1000 customers entering the store.

The past, the present, the future and uncertainty

Finding out what happened yesterday is a matter of historical research and of fact. Discovering what is happening today is also a matter of fact but accuracy is harder and more expensive to achieve. Predicting the future is unlikely to be completely accurate and has to be based on our knowledge of past and present trends and tendencies and our judgement of the extent to which these are likely to continue into the future. Past trends usually have to be modified when projected into the future. Accuracy depends on foreseeing and taking account of these modifying forces. There will always be some uncertainty and if major influences are not foreseen, inaccuracies can be significant. Consider, for example, the effects of the Iraqi invasion of Kuwait in 1990. The need to make judgements about an uncertain future gives business much of its fascination. However sophisticated the technology of information, business decision-making can never be completely mechanical.

Types of economy

Most economic decisions involve choices between competing uses for scarce resources. On the national scale there are two main methods of making these decisions and these give rise to two main kinds of economic structure.

The market economy

Here resources are directed towards uses selected by individual competing enterprises in accordance with the judgements they make of the most advantageous ways of providing people with those goods and services they appear to want and are prepared to make sacrifices of their own resources to obtain.

The planned economy

Here resources are directed towards uses selected by the political machinery of the State in accordance with judgements made by whichever individuals or groups effectively control this machinery.

Mixed economies

In practice no economy allows all its economic decisions to be made by totally unregulated markets and very few economies have survived for any great length of time under a totally planned structure. Most, therefore, are mixtures of planned and market systems but the proportions of the mix and the relationships between the structures are often highly controversial.

Today the prevailing climate favours the market structure and it is mostly this that is examined in this course though some important aspects of the planned sector are also considered.

Features of the market economy

Individuals and households are free to buy or not to buy goods and services according to the judgement they make about the degree of satisfaction or **utility** which they gain from acquiring them. It is assumed that people:

- seek to **maximise their utility,** i.e. to achieve the highest possible level of satisfaction from the sacrifice of their own resources of income and wealth which can be spent on purchases of consumer goods and services in markets.
- are rational in the sense earlier defined, at least as far as their group purchasing behaviour is concerned.

Goods and services are supplied by enterprises which are largely free to choose what to produce, the quantity and the method of production. These enterprises seek to achieve the objectives of their owners and/or managers through the decisions they reach about production and the prices they charge in the market.

Market forces

There are thus two forces interacting within the market economy. There is the force of **demand** fuelled by the desire of individuals and households to spend their available money on goods and services. There is also the force of **supply** fuelled by pressure from enterprises to maximise their own utility, which initially, but to be modified later, is assumed to be **profit**. The study of this interaction and its implications is the subject of the next topic. The **market** is the term employed for any area within which those prepared to buy certain goods or services are able to communicate with those prepared to sell those goods and services. As communications technology develops, market areas tend to become larger. Some products, e.g. financial securities effectively trade in a world market.

Discussion and revision questions

Enterprise is often classed as a fourth factor of production with its reward given as profit. Discuss the problems that may arise if this classification is adopted. Consider the following

- What actually is 'enterprise'? Does it mean risk taking? If so, do gamblers always succeed in making profits? Should business managers, who are essentially using other people's money take or avoid risks?

- Does profit only arise as a result of enterprise?

- Can organisations show enterprise or is it purely a quality of individuals?

- Is there any link between enterprise and profit in the case of large organisations?

- Can state-controlled organisations show enterprise?

- Is there such a thing as a 'free lunch'?

- 'Opportunity cost is one of the easiest of economic concepts to understand but one of the hardest to measure and put to practical use.' Is this true? If it is, suggest why.

- Business management has been described as the skill of making decisions under conditions of uncertainty? Why is there uncertainty and how does it arise?

- Why do you think there appears to be a close association between belief in the market economy and in political democracy?

2

Demand

Topic summary

The flow of demand

A want does not necessarily constitute demand. For demand to exist people must be able and willing to sacrifice sufficient of their own resources to obtain the required good. This is true even in markets which do not depend on money as the medium of exchange. In a pioneering country demand for houses exists when the pioneers start to devote their resources of time and energy to cutting trees and building houses. In a modern economy, based on money, demand for a good exists when people demonstrate willingness and ability to pay to obtain the good. In a market controlled by the State, demand for a good exists when a political decision is taken to devote resources to the production of that good.

The demand schedule

Demand is related to a clearly defined good (production factor, product or service) in a particular market area over a stated period of time. In unregulated markets it results from large numbers of decisions about whether or not to buy at the relevant price. A demand schedule, therefore, should show the quantities of the good that people in the market are prepared to buy within the relevant period, at various prices within the range under review.

A simple demand schedule might take the following form:

Demand for widgetts in London superstores	
Price per widgett *(£)*	*Quantity per week* *(numbers of widgetts)*
10	200
9	400
8	600
7	800
6	1000

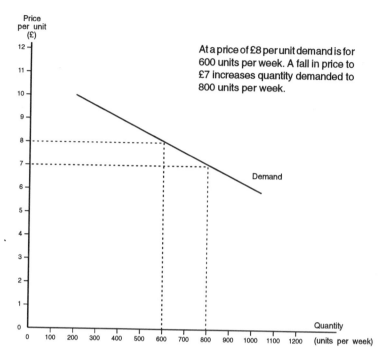

At a price of £8 per unit demand is for 600 units per week. A fall in price to £7 increases quantity demanded to 800 units per week.

Figure 2.1 Demand for widgetts

This schedule is the basis for the demand curve of Figure 2.1. Notice the direction of slope of this curve. This results from the assumption that more of a **normal** good will be bought at a lower than at a higher price, other things being equal. Notice also that this example illustrates a **linear** (straight line relationship) and it uses just a selection of prices within a range which is relevant for the good under consideration. These assumptions are useful for analysis at most introductory levels and are reasonably realistic. Economists will look for a **line of best fit** through data showing demand for actual products and, where possible, they will look for a linear relationship. Unless, therefore, there is a good reason to do otherwise you should draw simple straight line demand curves. The term curve, incidentally derives from conventional mathematical terminology and includes straight lines.

Demand functions

If there is a clear relationship between changes in price and changes in quantity sold this can also be expressed in algebraic form. In the example shown above the quantity of widgetts sold (Q_w) can be found from the equation:

$$Q_w = 2200 - 200P_w \quad \text{where } P_w = \text{ the price of each widgett}$$

This is just an application of the general equation of a linear curve, $Q = a + bP$ where a is the constant value for Q when $P = 0$ and b is the slope of the curve which here is negative (-200).

Mathematicians sometimes object that the dependent variable (quantity is here assumed to depend on price) should, by convention, be measured along the vertical not the horizontal axis. One possible reason for this apparent reversal of the normal practice is that price and quantity should be seen as being dependent on each other. Neither should be regarded as dependent or independent. The business manager (or the interaction of market forces) can adjust either or both according to judgement. Neither is usually predetermined. A major advantage of portraying demand in algebraic form as opposed to the traditional geometric form of the demand curve is that algebraic models are suitable for computer-aided analysis. Most students, however, still find it helpful to visualise relationships and the implications of shifts in relationships through the usual geometric or graphical illustrations.

Influences on demand

Only one influence, the good's own price, has been assumed so far. Clearly there must be others. It is usual to identify a limited number of major influences and most others are seen as operating through one of the following:

Prices of other goods

If goods are substitutes (e.g. rail and motor coach travel) then a rise in the price of one can be expected to lead to a rise in demand for the other. If they are complementary (e.g. houses and furniture) then a rise in the price of one is likely to lead to a fall in the demand for the other. If a good is regarded as a regular and necessary purchase from income (e.g. petrol or the cost of servicing a mortgage) then a rise in the price of one will reduce demand for a wide range of other goods with which it has no direct association. All consumer goods are in competition for a share of disposable income.

Disposable income

Disposable income is that amount of income left after payment of taxes and 'near taxes' such as national insurance and compulsory pension contributions. Some would argue that the more relevant figure is **discretionary income** which is that part of disposable income left after payment of regular, essential items such as mortgage interest, household and car insurance, fuel bills and the cost of basic food and travel to work. Discretionary income is a great deal lower than gross or even disposable income and is affected by many more pressures, such as interest rates and petrol prices, but it is the amount that permits — or restricts — peoples' ability to purchase discretionary items such as holidays, meals out, new furnishings, home decorations and so on.

Consequently demand for these items can fluctuate violently following, say, a significant rise in interest rates. Normally, changes in income and demand can be expected to move in the same direction but there are some exceptions such as those regarded as **inferior** to preferred substitutes. A worker may travel to work by car instead of cycling as income rises but revert to the bicycle if discretionary income contracts. Demand for bicycles may thus move in the opposite direction from income changes.

The supply and cost of money and credit

Many durable goods and the more expensive services are bought under credit schemes. Where these are readily available demand is likely to rise. A credit contraction will have a depressing effect on consumer buying.

Marketing effort

Nothing sells itself. The greater the effort made to market and sell a product the more likely the achievement of a high level of demand.

Market size and communications

The larger the area within which suppliers can communicate with potential buyers the greater the probable sales. Changes in the age structure of a community can affect the demand for goods which appeal to particular age groups.

Fashion or taste

This includes short-term fashions e.g. for clothing and footwear or pop records but also takes account of longer term trends such as attitudes to health, foods, tobacco, wine and meat.

Other influences

Demand for some goods, such as soft drinks or ice cream, is subject to special influences such as weather.

General demand function

These ideas can be summarised in the expression:

$$Q = f(P_o, P_a, Y_d, M, A, N, T, v)$$

where P_o = the good's own price
P_a = the prices of other goods or services
Y_d = disposable or discretionary income
M = the availability and cost of money/credit
A = the marketing effort made by supplier(s)
N = the number of potential buyers (market size)
T = taste and fashion
v = any relevant, special influences such as weather

In turn, this general demand function can be the basis for a demand equation for a specific good. This equation shows the relative strengths of the significant influences on demand for a particular good.

$$Q_x = aP_o + bP_a + cY_d + dM + eA$$

In this case only the first five of the general influences are regarded as significant for this particular product. The firm able to estimate the values of these coefficients and predict, with reasonable accuracy, future movements in each influence will have a fair prospect of making useful estimates of future demand.

Demand elasticities

You can now see the importance of being able to measure the strength of the various pressures on demand. The most commonly used measures of demand are the elasticities of demand. Elasticity can be calculated for any quantifiable influence but the main ones in practical use relate to prices and incomes.

Price elasticity of demand (E_d)

$$E_d = \frac{\text{The proportional change in quantity (Q) demanded of a good}}{\text{The proportional change in the price (P) of the good}}$$

This can be expressed by the formula:

$E_d = \dfrac{\Delta Q}{Q} \div \dfrac{\Delta P}{P}$ the Greek letter Δ signifying a change in a variable.

The formula can be arranged as:

$E_d = \dfrac{P\Delta Q}{Q\Delta P}$ or, if you are familiar with simple differential calculus,

as $\dfrac{PdQ}{QdP}$

Since, for normal goods, the quantity change will be in the reverse direction to the price change (e.g. a price rise will lead to a quantity fall) the correct elasticity calculation carries a – sign.

Remember, however, the negative (–) sign indicates **only the direction of change**. The **strength** of the quantity reaction to the price change is indicated by the elasticity figure produced by the equation. The closer this is to zero (0), the weaker the reaction. When the elasticity value is between 0 and 1 (ignoring the – sign) demand is said to be **price inelastic**. When it is over 1, demand is said to be **price elastic** and when it is 1, i.e. when the proportional changes in both quantity and price are the same, it is said to be **unitary**. The fact that there is some reaction, as there almost always will be, **does not** signify that demand is elastic. You must observe the conventions set out above.

It is sometimes pointed out that there are cases when a price change appears to produce a quantity change in the same direction and it is claimed that goods where this appears to occur are Giffen goods. In such cases, however, the usual reason lies in another change (or changes) taking place at the same time and these are more powerful than the price change effect and produce a total shift in the same direction as price. The most common would be changes in income or the prices of other goods. Occasionally price is perceived as an indicator of quality to produce a similar effect.

You should also be aware that the slope of a demand curve can be an unreliable guide to the demand elasticity of a good. This normally (and **always** if the curve is linear) changes as price changes (see Figure 2.2).

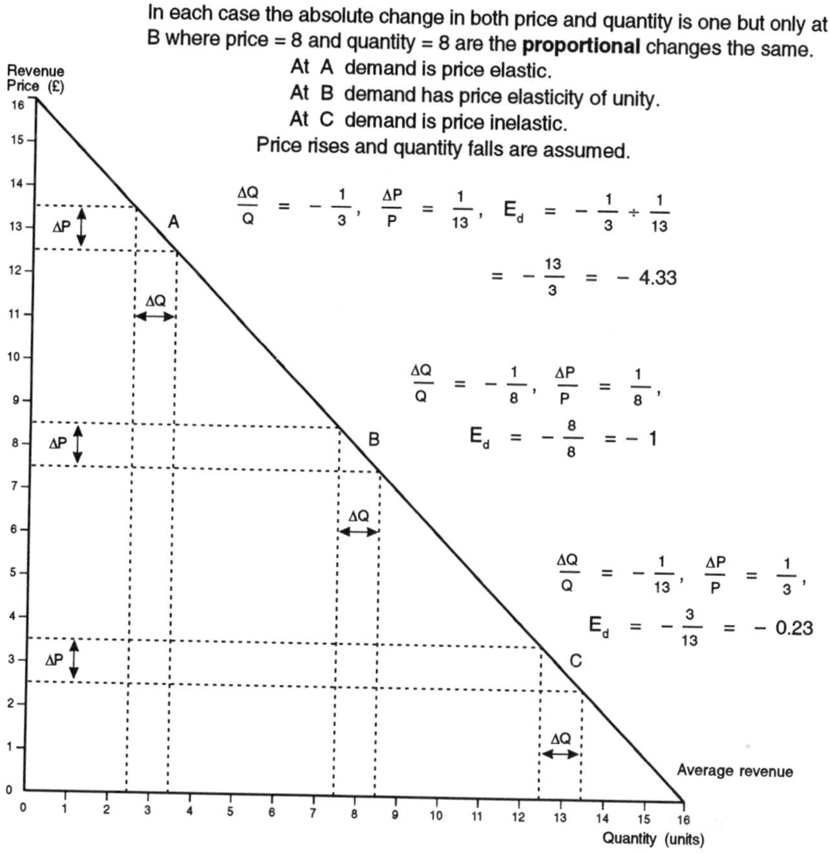

In each case the absolute change in both price and quantity is one but only at B where price = 8 and quantity = 8 are the **proportional** changes the same.

At A demand is price elastic.
At B demand has price elasticity of unity.
At C demand is price inelastic.
Price rises and quantity falls are assumed.

$$\frac{\Delta Q}{Q} = -\frac{1}{3}, \quad \frac{\Delta P}{P} = \frac{1}{13}, \quad E_d = -\frac{1}{3} \div \frac{1}{13}$$

$$= -\frac{13}{3} = -4.33$$

$$\frac{\Delta Q}{Q} = -\frac{1}{8}, \quad \frac{\Delta P}{P} = \frac{1}{8},$$

$$E_d = -\frac{8}{8} = -1$$

$$\frac{\Delta Q}{Q} = -\frac{1}{13}, \quad \frac{\Delta P}{P} = \frac{1}{3},$$

$$E_d = -\frac{3}{13} = -0.23$$

Figure 2.2 Price elasticity of demand

The special case where $E_d = -1$ throughout the length of the curve is shown in Figure 2.3

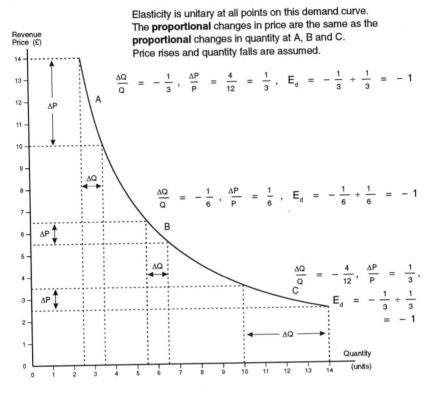

Figure 2.3 Demand curve with unitary elasticity

Income elasticity of demand (E_y)

Precisely the same reasoning and methods of calculation are applied to this elasticity which is calculated from the formula:

$$E_y = \frac{\Delta Q}{Q} \div \frac{\Delta Y}{Y} \quad \text{where } Q = \text{quantity and } Y = \text{disposable income}$$

For normal goods the quantity and income changes will be in the same direction. Higher incomes enable more of most things to be bought. However, a rise in income may enable consumers to switch to preferred substitutes (e.g. rail or air travel instead of long distance coach). The good abandoned when incomes rise (and resumed when they fall) is known as an **inferior** good. This is not a reflection on its quality, just on its perception by consumers. Thus the income elasticity of demand for normal goods is positive and for inferior goods it is negative.

Cross elasticity of demand ($E_{x,y}$)

This relates the quantity change in one good (Q_x) to a price change in another (P_y) so that the cross demand elasticity ($E_{x,y}$) formula becomes:

$$E_{x,y} = \frac{\Delta Q_x}{Q_x} \div \frac{\Delta P_y}{P_y}$$

The same conventions as before apply to the signs signifying direction of change and the application of the terms elastic and inelastic to the value measure. A negative sign thus indicates that the demand for X and Y are associated and they are known as **complementary goods** or **complements** whereas a positive value indicates that they are **substitutes** (e.g. a rise in the price of beef is likely to lead to a rise in the quantity demanded of lamb).

Point and arc calculations

When it is desired to measure elasticity at a particular point on the demand curve and the movement of price and quantity is only very small, it is legitimate to base the calculations on the price and quantity levels before the changes. The difference between considering the effect of a price rise will not then be materially different from considering a price fall. However, when there is a relatively substantial change in either price or quantity, proportional changes based on a price rise will differ from those based on a price fall. In these cases arc elasticity calculations should then be made in which the midpoints of change for both price and quantity are used, i.e. $Q = (Q_1 + Q_2)/2$ and $P = (P_1 + P_2)/2$ where P_1 and Q_1 are the prices and quantities before the change and P_2 and Q_2 are the prices and quantities after the change.

Similar point and arc calculations can be made for income and cross-price elasticities of demand.

Demand and revenue

When a firm makes a sale it earns a revenue. The term revenue is used to signify the money received from sales before the deduction of any of the costs of operation.

Average revenue

This is the total revenue received from sales during a specified period divided by the number of items sold. If all items are sold at the same price at any given time for any given level of sales then average revenue is the same as price and the demand curve for the individual firm is also that firm's average revenue curve. If the firm can sell at any quantity level within a relevant range at the same price its average revenue curve will be horizontal as shown in Figure 2.4. If it has to reduce price in order to sell an increased quantity its average revenue curve will be downward sloping as shown in Figure 2.5.

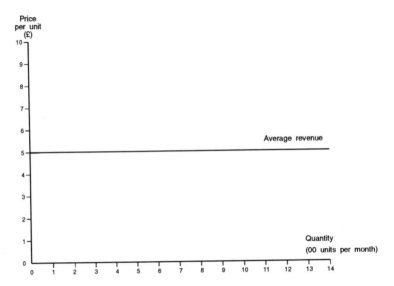

Figure 2.4 The firm sells at any quantity level up to 1400 units per month at the same price per unit

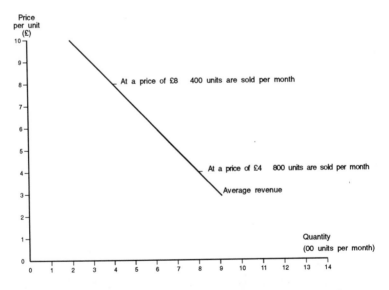

Figure 2.5 The firm can sell higher quantities if it reduces price

Total revenue

This is the total receipts from sales as the quantity sold rises during a specified period. The total revenue curves derived from Figures 2.4 and 2.5 are shown in Figures 2.6 and 2.7. Notice that the total revenue from sales when price falls as quantity sold rises reaches a peak (at the 600 units per month level in Figure 2.6). If a firm seeks to sell at a higher quantity level than 600 units per month, the price reduction necessary to increase quantity sold will start to reduce the total revenue received.

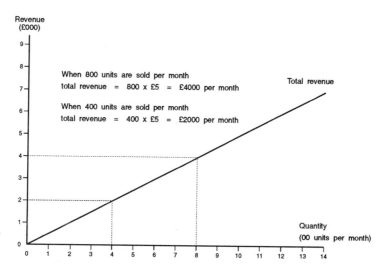

Figure 2.6 Total revenue where price is unchanged
at each quantity level

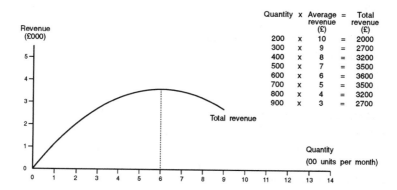

Figure 2.7 Total revenue when the firm has to reduce
price to sell at higher quantity level

Marginal revenue

Marginal revenue (MR) is the change in total revenue as quantity sold changes. It is always related to the smallest possible change in quantity, i.e. a change of one unit. When a sales schedule shows steps as in the examples below it is necessary to divide the total revenue change from one step to another by the number of units in that step. Marginal revenue is thus the change in total revenue divided by the change in quantity sold. This can be expressed as:

$$MR = \frac{\Delta TR}{\Delta Q}$$

Below is the full schedule of revenues on which Figures 2.5, 2.7 and 2.8 are based. Figure 2.8 shows the marginal revenue with the average revenue of Figure 2.5 extended to meet both axes.

1	2	3 (2 x 1)	4 ($\Delta 3 \div \Delta 1$)
Quantity (Units)	Average Revenue (£)	Total Revenue (£)	Marginal Revenue (£)
200	10	2000	
			7
300	9	2700	
			5
400	8	3200	
			3
500	7	3500	
			1
600	6	3600	
			− 1
700	5	3500	
			− 3
800	4	3200	
			− 5
900	3	2700	

Note that marginal revenue = 0 at the quantity level of 600 units per month, i.e. exactly half the quantity level (1200 units per month) where average revenue = 0. This is not accidental. When the average revenue curve is linear the marginal revenue curve will slope twice as steeply and **bisect** the horizontal distance between the average revenue curve and the vertical, revenue axis. Figure 2.9 provides a geometric proof followed by a brief proof using simple differential calculus.

Where the firm is able to sell all units of the product within its output range **at the same price** then, of course, the marginal revenue is the same as the average revenue which is the same as the unit price.

Elasticity and revenue

In the above example marginal revenue = 0 at quantity level 600 and it is at this level that total revenue is at its maximum of £3600. For output levels below 600, marginal revenue, though falling, is still positive so any additional

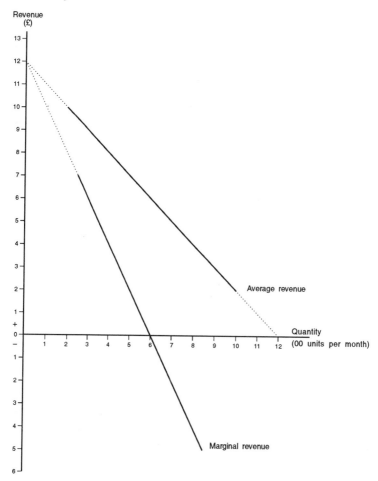

Figure 2.8 Marginal revenue and average revenue
Note the quantity level where marginal revenue = 0

output still increases total revenue. For output levels above 600 marginal revenue is negative so further additions of output must **reduce** total revenue. Look back at Figure 2.7 and you will see that at this output level of 600 the total revenue curve peaks so that its slope at this point is 0. Since the marginal revenue curve represents the slope of the total revenue curve its value at this turning point must be 0 as indicated in the schedule.

Look back now to Figure 2.2. This shows that price elasticity of demand was unitary at the quantity level 8, again half that of the level (16) where average revenue = 0. At output levels below 800, where demand is **price elastic**, the proportional change in quantity is greater than the proportional change in price so a price reduction in this sector **increases** total revenue. For quantity levels above 800, where demand is **price inelastic** the proportional change in quantity is less than the proportional

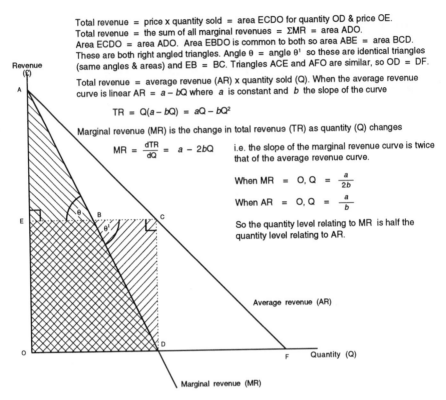

Total revenue = price x quantity sold = area ECDO for quantity OD & price OE.
Total revenue = the sum of all marginal revenues = ΣMR = area ADO.
Area ECDO = area ADO. Area EBDO is common to both so area ABE = area BCD.
These are both right angled triangles. Angle θ = angle θ¹ so these are identical triangles
(same angles & areas) and EB = BC. Triangles ACE and AFO are similar, so OD = DF.

Total revenue = average revenue (AR) x quantity sold (Q). When the average revenue
curve is linear AR = $a - bQ$ where a is constant and b the slope of the curve

$$TR = Q(a - bQ) = aQ - bQ^2$$

Marginal revenue (MR) is the change in total revenue (TR) as quantity (Q) changes

$$MR = \frac{dTR}{dQ} = a - 2bQ$$

i.e. the slope of the marginal revenue curve is twice that of the average revenue curve.

When $MR = 0, Q = \frac{a}{2b}$

When $AR = 0, Q = \frac{a}{b}$

So the quantity level relating to MR is half the quantity level relating to AR.

Figure 2.9 The average and marginal revenue curves

change in price and any further increase in quantity achieved by a price reduction must **reduce** total revenue. Given this demand curve, therefore, **revenue is maximised where E$_d$ = – 1 which is also where MR = 0.**

This gives the important general rule that where:

- the price-quantity relationship is linear
- firms do **not** price discriminate, i.e. where all buyers at any given quantity level are charged the same price

revenue is maximised when the price elasticity of demand is at unity.

Discussion and revision questions

- Draw the demand curve corresponding to the demand equation

$$Q = 500 - 50P$$

- Outline what you would expect to be the four main influences on the demand for the following and justify your selections: package holidays in the Mediterranean countries; 2 seater sports cars; children's videotapes; Scotch whisky.

- In the period 1989-90 the British government forced up interest rates to high levels in the belief that this would curb the excess demand that was believed to be causing dangerously rapid price rises. On what grounds could it be argued that high interest rates would reduce consumer demand?

- What changes have been taking place in the structure of the population in Britain over the past twenty years? How have these changes affected the general pattern of consumer demand for goods and services?

- Calculate the price elasticities of demand for the following
  - A price reduction of 10% brings about an increase in sales from 500 articles per week to 540 per week..
  - An increase in price from £15 per article to £20, leads to a fall in sales from 300 per week to 250.
  - A butcher reports that most of the shop's regular customers keep their expenditure on meat each week unchanged, regardless of shifting meat prices.

- Calculate the income or cross elasticities for the following
  - A reduction in income tax led to an increase in disposable income of 5% and this produced a rise in spending on holidays abroad of 4%.
  - A rise of 25% in the price of coffee led to an increase in sales of drinking chocolate and similar products of 15%.
  - A general rise in wages 5% greater than the level of price rises led to a fall in sales of the standard white sliced loaf of bread of 2%.

- Complete the following table and draw the related total, average and marginal revenue curves. Assume the firm charges all customers the same price at any given level of sales.

Quantity (units per week)	Price per unit (£)	Total Revenue (£)	Marginal Revenue (£)
150	11		
200	10		
250	9		
300	8		
350	7		
400	6		
450	5		
500	4		

If the company wishes to maximise revenue on sales of this product what price should it charge?
What will be the price elasticity of demand of the product at this price?
What is the demand function relevant to this quantity-price schedule?

- Under what conditions can a producer continue to increase production and sales and still continue to increase revenue?

- What is the relationship between a linear average revenue curve and the marginal revenue curve that can be derived from it?

Multiple choice questions

- A product has a point price elasticity of demand of -0.8. The producer decides to increase price from £5 to £5.50 per unit. At the £5 price monthly sales were 500 units. As a result of the price increase the total monthly sales revenue can be expected to

  A remain unchanged
  B rise by £470
  C fall by £500
  D rise by £30

- A product has an income elasticity of 0.4. As a result of an income tax reduction the average disposable income of buyers rises by 6%. Total sales of the product can be expected to:

  A remain unchanged
  B rise by 2.4%
  C fall by 0.4%
  D rise by 15%

- A product whose demand curve is downward sloping, has a price elasticity of demand of -1.3%. Its producer, wishing to increase the revenue from sales of the product should:

  A raise price and increase the quantity produced
  B raise price and reduce the quantity produced
  C reduce price and increase the quantity produced
  D reduce price and reduce the quantity produced

- A product whose demand curve is horizontal has a price elasticity of demand of:

  A infinity
  B 1
  C zero
  D -1

- If two products are regarded as substitutes their cross elasticities of demand must be:

  A negative
  B positive
  C between 0 and 1
  D greater than 1

3

Supply

Topic summary

Supply decisions

Supply decisions are made by firms in accordance with their view of the most rewarding way to use the resources at their disposal. Whereas with demand it was assumed that as price rises, the quantity people are willing to buy falls, for supply it is assumed that as price rises the quantity firms are willing to produce and offer to the market is likely to rise.

The supply schedule

As with demand these decisions can be represented in the form of a schedule.

A simple supply schedule might take the following form:

Supply of widgetts to London superstores	
Price per widgett (£)	Quantity per week (numbers of widgetts)
5	200
6	400
7	600
8	800
9	1000

The supply curve

This schedule is the basis for the supply curve of Figure 3.1. Notice the direction of the curve which slopes upwards from left to right. This reflects the assumption that, other things being unchanged, an increase in price leads suppliers to increase the quantity supplied to the market. For the same reasons and with the same justification as the demand curve which you have already examined, the supply curve is always represented as a straight line (linear curve) unless there is a good reason to do otherwise.

Supply functions

The equation of the curve of Figure 3.1 showing the quantity of widgetts Q_w that will be supplied at each price is:

$$Q_w = -800 + 200P_w \quad \text{where } P_w = \text{ the price per widgett}$$

-800 is the constant representing the value of Q when $P = 0$ and 200 is the slope of the curve.

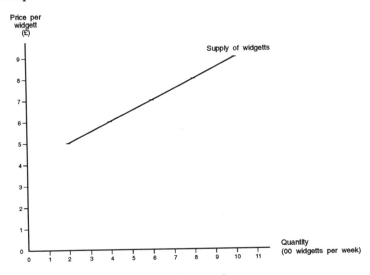

Figure 3.1 The supply curve

Influences on supply

Price, although a powerful influence on supply, is not the only variable likely to influence the decisions of suppliers to a market. Others include:

Cost of production factors and inputs

Goods and services have to be produced and any change in the cost of production must affect supply decisions. If suppliers have to pay more for inputs they will try to recover this amount from buyers to maintain their own profit returns. This is illustrated in Figure 3.2.

In Figure 3.2 there is an increase in input costs equivalent to £1 per widgett at each production level. Consequently the supply curve moves up by the vertical distance equal to £1, from S_0 to S_1. As a result the quantity supplied at price £7 falls from 600 to 400 widgetts per week. To keep supply at 600 widgetts the price would have to rise from £7 to £8. If there were a reduction in input price equivalent to £1 per widgett then the effect can be seen by assuming that the supply curve moves from S_1 to S_0.

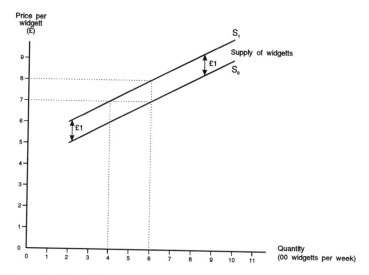

Figure 3.2 The shift in supply curve following an increase in input cost

Expenditure or production tax

If a tax, such as VAT, customs or excise duty, is imposed at any stage of production, including the final stage of distribution to the consumer, the effect will be the same as an increase in input cost. If the tax is reduced or if a subsidy (payment to producers by the Government) is paid or increased, the effect will be as for a reduction in input cost, i.e. movement from S_1 to S_0.

Change in the prices of other goods

Firms will supply widgetts if they perceive this to be the most rewarding use for the resources at their disposal. If conditions change so that producing something else becomes more rewarding, usually as a result of relative changes in price, firms can be expected to change their supply intentions. Some supply resources will switch to the more attractive market and there will be a shift of the supply curve in the direction of S_0 to S_1, illustrated in Figure 3.2. Similarly, of course, if the widgett market becomes more attractive because other forms of production have become less rewarding then suppliers will switch from other markets to the supply of widgetts and the supply curve shift will be in the direction of S_1 to S_0.

Change in production technology

In the longer term one of the most powerful influences on supply is technology which enables firms to make existing products in new ways and to produce new goods and services with existing resources. New markets are created and supply conditions for old markets can change significantly. The new supply curve may be very different from the old.

Production technology is here given the widest possible meaning and includes managerial skills and information technology.

General supply function

As with demand these ideas form the basis for the general function:

$$Q = f(P_o, P_a, T_e, v)$$

where P_o = the good's own price
P_a = the prices of other goods
T_e = expenditure and production taxes
v = the level of technology

When it is possible to give values to these functional relationships a more specific equation for a particular good can be formed, e.g.

$$Q_x = aP_o + bP_a + cT_e + dv$$

The firm's problem, of course, is to put realistic values to these coefficients.

Supply elasticity

It is, of course, possible to use the device of elasticity to measure the strength of any of the variables determining supply but in practice at this stage of study it is normal to consider only price elasticity of supply (E_s) and for simplicity this can be referred to simply as elasticity of supply. The same conventions apply as with demand elasticities but as the supply curve has been assumed to be positively sloped, the elasticity value can always be expected to be positive and the sign is normally omitted. The supply elasticity equation is:

$$E_s = \frac{\text{the proportional change in quantity supplied of a good}}{\text{the proportional change in price of that good}}$$

This can be expressed as:

$$E_s = \frac{\Delta Q}{Q} \div \frac{\Delta P}{P} \text{ or } \frac{P\Delta Q}{Q\Delta P}$$

or, using the language of differential calculus

$$E_s = \frac{PdQ}{QdP}$$

If the above calculations produce a value which is less than 1, supply is said to be price inelastic, if more than 1 it is elastic and if $E_s = 1$ it is unitary.

Whereas with the linear demand curve elasticity could move from elastic, through unitary elasticity to inelastic along the same curve a linear supply curve is elastic, inelastic or unitary depending on its position relative to the point of origin of the graph. A supply curve which, when extended, passes through the vertical (price) axis is elastic. If it passes through the horizontal (quantity) axis it is inelastic and, if through the point of origin, it has unit elasticity. This rule holds regardless of the slopes of the curves and it is illustrated in figures 3.3, 3.4 and 3.5.

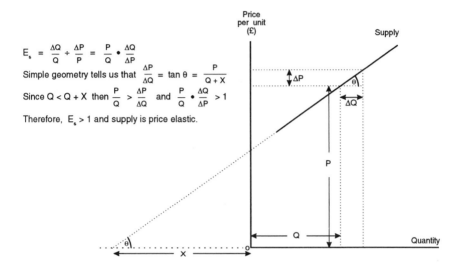

$$E_s = \frac{\Delta Q}{Q} \div \frac{\Delta P}{P} = \frac{P}{Q} \cdot \frac{\Delta Q}{\Delta P}$$

Simple geometry tells us that $\frac{\Delta P}{\Delta Q} = \tan \theta = \frac{P}{Q+X}$

Since $Q < Q + X$ then $\frac{P}{Q} > \frac{\Delta P}{\Delta Q}$ and $\frac{P}{Q} \cdot \frac{\Delta Q}{\Delta P} > 1$

Therefore, $E_s > 1$ and supply is price elastic.

Figure 3.3 An elastic supply curve

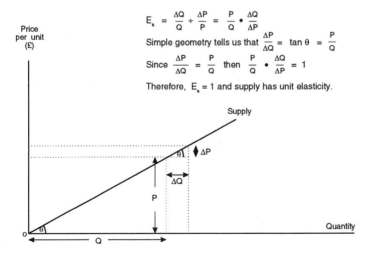

$$E_s = \frac{\Delta Q}{Q} \div \frac{\Delta P}{P} = \frac{P}{Q} \cdot \frac{\Delta Q}{\Delta P}$$

Simple geometry tells us that $\frac{\Delta P}{\Delta Q} = \tan \theta = \frac{P}{Q}$

Since $\frac{\Delta P}{\Delta Q} = \frac{P}{Q}$ then $\frac{P}{Q} \cdot \frac{\Delta Q}{\Delta P} = 1$

Therefore, $E_s = 1$ and supply has unit elasticity.

Figure 3.4 Supply curve with unit elasticity

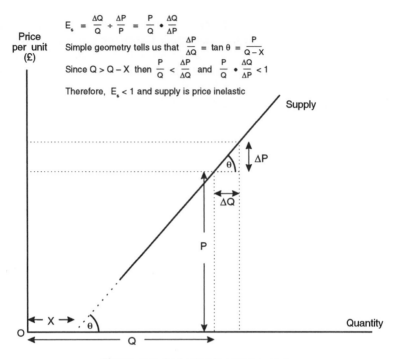

Figure 3.5 An inelastic supply curve

The comments relating to point and arc demand elasticity calculations also apply to supply elasticities.

The costs of supply

In order to understand and identify costs it is helpful to classify them. The more a producer knows about costs the greater the chance of controlling them in order to obtain maximum value from the resources employed. It is helpful to start with the broad divisions normally recognised by economists. The main examples used in this section are based on the production of a book. You should have no difficulty applying the ideas to other examples from sectors of production with which you are familiar.

Variable costs

These are the payments made for those inputs which vary directly with the quantity of output. The most obvious are the materials and components out of which the product is constructed. In the case of book production the main variable cost is that of printing the final copies and this includes the paper and copying costs and these can readily be identified and expressed as an amount per book. Other variable costs to the book publisher are the royalties paid to the author and commissions/discounts allowed to booksellers, export agents and salespeople, as these are almost invariably expressed as a rate per book. In practice the publisher usually treats these variable sales and distribution costs as deductions from revenue before arriving at the net revenue received from sales.

Fixed costs

These are fixed only in the sense that they do not vary with the quantity of the product produced. They are the same whether 500 or 5000 items are produced. In the case of a book the editing cost is fixed. It is based on the amount of time taken to edit the book either by a member of the publisher's staff or a free-lance editor. This depends on the size and complexity of the book and not on the number of copies to be printed. Cover design and payments to artists, photographers or other specialists are also fixed costs, as is the cost of typesetting, i.e producing the master copy on which all other copies will be based. The book is also expected to contribute to the fixed costs of the publisher's administration and to the cost of machinery used by the printer. Notice that many of these costs are **sunk** in the sense that once the decision has been made to publish the book, editors, designers and so on have to be paid when their work is complete. The costs cannot later be reduced if sales are poor or even if the decision is made to abandon publication or withdraw the book after a short period. Because the firm is vulnerable if it cannot meet high fixed costs and if it cannot keep fixed factors of production such as machines and specialist staff fully employed there has been a growing tendency in recent years to keep the sunk element to a minimum. For this reason most publishers now employ independent printing and typesetting firms and free-lance editors, designers and other specialists.

Total and average costs

Before deciding whether or not to publish any given book the publisher must calculate the total fixed costs, estimate how many copies are likely to be sold, use this estimate to decide the number of books to be printed and so calculate the total variable costs. The total variable and fixed costs are then combined to produce the total cost and this is divided by the number of copies to be printed to provide an average total cost. This is compared with the estimate of selling price likely to be acceptable to the market and if the difference offers a rate of profit acceptable to the publisher and if the sales projections are convincing and believed to be reliable then the book is likely to be published. Notice especially the following important facts:

- Average costs cannot be calculated without a decision on the number of items to be produced.
- The production estimate cannot be made without a prior estimate of the number of sales.
- Average cost calculations will only be as accurate as the sales estimate.

If only half the estimated number of sales can be achieved then the average costs related to sold books will be much higher than the original estimate and the contribution to profit, if any, will be much lower. Remember that all the fixed and many of the variable costs will have been sunk once the required number of copies of the book has been printed and delivered to the warehouse.

Production, marketing and distribution costs

Suppliers of most products usually find it essential to separate the actual costs of producing the product from those of marketing and distributing it, mainly because rather different considerations tend to apply. Once a production method has been established, design adopted and decisions made on the materials to be used, the total and average production costs are likely to remain stable for a given production run. The scope for altering distribution costs in the short term is also likely to be limited but marketing costs are more flexible. The supplier must decide how much to devote to market research, advertising and promotion. This involves consideration of their effectiveness and requires a thorough knowledge of the nature of demand for the product, i.e. the influences outlined in unit 2 and their relative importance.

The break-even point

Throughout this section you will have noticed the importance of sales quantity to the consideration of costs. This, of course, arises out of the sunk nature of many of the costs so that quantity sold will determine whether and how much profit is achieved. This is simply and easily illustrated through a break-even diagram of the kind shown in Figure 3.6. For simplicity this is based on the assumption that a clear distinction can be made between fixed and variable costs and that variable costs are a constant amount per unit throughout a given production range. If sales do not reach the level of Oq (total of fixed costs) within the firm's target period and there is no hope of future improvement the firm should cease production and try to transfer resources to something likely to be more profitable. If sales remain between Oq and Ox where at least a contribution is being made to the sunk, fixed costs, production may continue for a time, especially if there is an expectation of future improvement but losses are being suffered and cannot continue indefinitely. Only when sales exceed the level of Ox are profits being enjoyed — note that they can rise rapidly from relatively small increases in sales once the break-even point of Ox has been passed. For a book, of course, and any other item where a fixed quantity **batch** is produced, most of the costs are incurred when the decision to produce is made and there is no going back. This emphasises the risks involved and the need to make reliable estimates of sales.

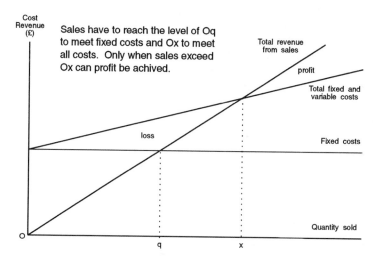

Figure 3.6 The break-even point

Marginal costs

This is an extremely important concept in both economics and business management. Marginal relates to the edge (margin) of a total. Marginal cost is the change in total cost when one more unit of output is produced. If you are familiar with the differential calculus it is the first differential of total cost with respect to changes in output, usually represented by the term dC/dQ (dC by dQ), where C = total cost and Q = the output level. In practice output can rarely be changed by a single unit. Production changes usually take place in steps of, say 100 or 1000 depending on the nature of the product. Consequently marginal cost is usually calculated by dividing the change in total cost by the change in output (the step in production level) represented by $\Delta C/\Delta Q$ where, as before, the symbol Δ = a change in a variable.

When rising marginal costs reach the level where the marginal cost is equal to the average total cost any further increase in marginal cost must also increase average cost. The rising marginal cost curve thus cuts the bottom of the average total cost curve. The point where marginal cost (MC) = average total cost (ATC) is the point of minimum average cost and is often referred to as the most efficient output level. This is illustrated in Figure 3.7.

Costs in the short and long run

There is a major distinction between the short and long run, again because it lays stress on commitment to sunk costs. The short run is that period during which at least one production factor is held constant. Production in the short term is thus limited by the capacity of the fixed factor-machinery, land or skilled manager or specialist. If attempts are made to continue to add more increments of the variable factors in this situation the firm will experience what is probably the best known of all economic concepts — diminishing returns. The more accurate term is diminishing marginal returns, marginal referring to increments at the edge (at the margin) of total production. For example, if more and more workers are added to a single factory and fixed number of machines, after a point each additional worker would add less to total production than the previous one until eventually a maximum would be reached and any further workers would actually reduce output. This is not a reflection on the quality of the workers but a result of an imbalance of production factors.

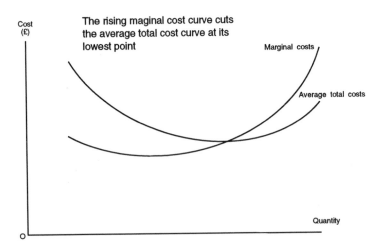

Figure 3.7 Marginal and average total cost

Note that if diminishing marginal returns are being experienced, i.e. if constant increments of an input produce progressively less output then it must cost progressively more to achieve a constant increment of output. Consequently **diminishing marginal returns give rise to increasing marginal costs**.

If the firm wishes to increase output beyond the limitation imposed by the fixed production factor it must increase **all** factors, i.e. acquire more space, machines, skilled labour or whatever was the limiting constraint. The long run is that period in which all factors can be changed. An increase in one or more fixed factors will, of course, increase fixed costs and will put the firm on a new short-run average total cost curve. The result, in the case of the successful firm will be to open up the possibility of achieving a long-run average total cost curve which is L-shaped (illustrated in Figure 3.8) as opposed to the typical U shape of the short-run average cost curve of Figure 3.7.

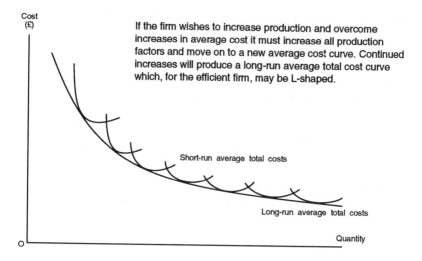

Cost
(£)

If the firm wishes to increase production and overcome increases in average cost it must increase all production factors and move on to a new average cost curve. Continued increases will produce a long-run average total cost curve which, for the efficient firm, may be L-shaped.

Short-run average total costs

Long-run average total costs

Quantity

O

Figure 3.8 Short- and long-run average total cost

Crucial decisions have to be made at the critical output levels where the firm has to choose whether or not to limit growth or move on to the new average cost curve. It must decide whether or not it can increase sales sufficiently to justify the additional fixed costs which, once incurred, are sunk and cannot be recovered. In many cases today firms are able to avoid having to make irreversible decisions by hiring or leasing additional vehicles, equipment, etc. rather than buying it. If the increased output level cannot be maintained the position is less hazardous and crippling losses are avoided.

Returns to scale

Returns to scale refer to the effect on output of increases in all factor inputs. Clearly there are three possibilities. An increase in inputs of a given proportion, say 10% may lead to a higher proportional output, say 15%, the same 10% increase in output or a smaller proportional output increase, say 5%. Each possibility has certain implications.

Increasing returns — economies of scale

Notice that genuine or real economies are only achieved if the increase in output is proportionally higher than the increase in inputs. These should be distinguished from pecuniary economies, i.e. financial savings achieved from exploiting market power through securing special discounts, etc. Real economies can be achieved by the more efficient management of land, equipment or labour, often through the ability of large firms to employ highly specialised management and keep it fully employed. Care is always needed to avoid being tempted by promises of scale economies to push up production to a level that cannot be sustained by sales. To return to the book example, printers usually offer substantial savings on unit cost for large production runs. Once the equipment has been set up the increase in cost to print 10 000 books is substantially less than twice the cost of printing 5000. However, the publisher who prints 10 000 copies of a book but manages to sell only 4000, is not likely to remain in business very long.

Increasing real returns are often known as **internal** economies of scale to distinguish them from **external economies** arising from the ability to hire specialist factors as required from within an industry or region.

The largest internal economies are normally achieved as the firm moves from small- to large-scale production. When further growth is achieved the gains become less significant — as illustrated in Figure 3.8.

Constant returns

The concept of the L-shaped long-run average cost curve suggests that over substantial ranges of output the average cost can be kept roughly constant. There are no further economies but no diseconomies either. The output level where significant economies of scale cease to be achieved is often termed the **minimum efficient scale (MES)** of operations. It is difficult to justify continued growth beyond the MES on efficiency grounds nor will one large firm operating above MES have any technical or production advantage over another operating at the same or higher level. If firms do continue to grow, therefore, there must be reasons other than cost advantage to account for the tendency.

Decreasing returns — diseconomies of scale

Continued growth is likely to lead to organisational problems related to managerial failures, often associated with breakdowns in communications and lack of co-ordination. If the firm continues to grow in spite of scale diseconomies the long-run average cost curve will start to rise and revert to the U shape of the short-run curve. This represents a challenge to management which the most successful teams will meet successfully.

The production of services

The economic implications of business costs are usually explained most easily in terms of manufacturing production but we have to recognise the increasing importance of services in modern economies. Most service organisations today face the same critical planning decisions as manufacturers as a result of their reliance on computers and other forms of electronic equipment. To expand beyond a critical point more advanced and more expensive equipment and more skilled staff are likely to be needed. The problem remains that of whether sales can be increased sufficiently to meet the resulting large 'step' in fixed costs. Service organisations may also move to an L-shaped long-run average cost curve but problems of communication and co-ordination are often greater and likely to lead to a resumption of the U shape until management learns to overcome the problems.

Revenue, cost and profit

In its simplest terms profit is the amount of revenue remaining when all costs have been met, i.e. Profit = Revenue (R) – Cost (C). The amount of profit at any given quantity level (Q) can be found from deducting total cost at that level from total revenue or from the product of quantity and average revenue (AR) – average cost (AC), i.e. Profit = Q(AR–AC).

When the firm is producing at the quantity level where marginal revenue (MR) = marginal cost (MC), it must be **maximising** its profit for the prevailing demand and supply conditions. This is illustrated in Figure 3.9.

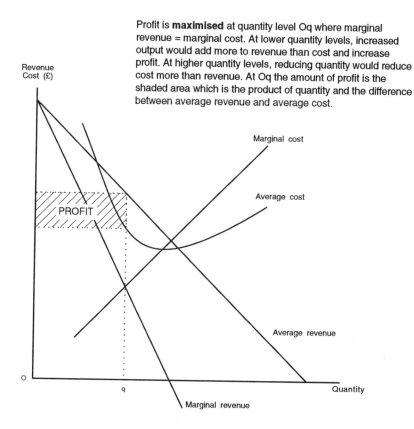

Profit is **maximised** at quantity level Oq where marginal revenue = marginal cost. At lower quantity levels, increased output would add more to revenue than cost and increase profit. At higher quantity levels, reducing quantity would reduce cost more than revenue. At Oq the amount of profit is the shaded area which is the product of quantity and the difference between average revenue and average cost.

Figure 3.9 Profit and profit maximisation

Discussion and revision questions

- Draw the supply curve corresponding to the supply equation

  $Q_S = 100 + 25P$

- The long-run average cost curve representing the unit cost of production is often shown to be L shaped, i.e. increased output reduces unit cost. However, the normal supply curve is usually assumed to be upward, positively sloped, indicating that firms only increase output in response to an increase in unit price. Suggest how this apparent contradiction might be reconciled.

- What shape will be the supply curve of a firm which is not able to change its supply in the short run?

- Explain with appropriate diagrams the effect on supply of the following:
  · a government decision to pay a subsidy to producers; reduced production costs brought about by developments in technology; a trade union secures a large wage increase for key production workers; the government reduces the standard rate of income tax.

- What do you consider to be the most important influences on the supply of the following?

  farm workers; electronics engineers; scotch whisky; new private houses.

- In the short run supply is highly inelastic but in the long run it tends to become more elastic. Explain this statement with the help of an appropriate diagram.

- Under what conditions, if any, would you expect the price elasticity of supply to be negative?

- What do you consider to be the most important influences on the price elasticity of supply?

- Label the following supply equations elastic (E), inelastic (I) or unitary elasticity (U).

  $Q_S = 200 + 50P$; $Q_S = 50 + 25P$; $Q_S = 100P$; $Q_S = -50 + 50P$

  Justify your decisions.

- Classify the following as fixed (F), variable (V) or part fixed and part variable (P) costs:
  · vehicle operation costs; plant depreciation; wages of a word processor operator; fuel and light costs for factory or office; advertising costs; managerial salaries.

- Under what conditions, if any, would a firm continue to produce a product when its average total cost was higher than the best price at which it can be sold?

- A firm is considering production of product X. This would involve fixed production costs of £50 000, variable production costs of £2 per unit, distribution costs of £0.50 per unit and marketing-promotional expenditure estimated at £20 000. Because of competition the most favourable unit price is believed to be £6.

  What level of sales would be needed to achieve the break-even point?
  What level of sales would provide a profit of £14 000?
  What level of sales would double this profit to £28 000?
  Comment on these findings.

- Which firm is the more vulnerable to a sudden collapse in the demand for its products, one with a high proportion of capital to labour or one with a high proportion of labour to capital?

- Under what circumstances would you consider it more desirable for a firm to hire rather than buy vehicles and equipment?

- If constant returns to scale are being achieved what can you say about the relationship between marginal and average cost?

- Discuss ways in which you think large companies might seek to avoid diseconomies of scale.

- What fixed costs would you expect to find in the following:
  - an insurance broker's office; a ladies' hairdressing salon; a travel agent's office; a sports centre?
    Discuss any similarities and differences suggested by your answer to the above.

- Why, in general, are manufacturers likely to achieve greater economies of scale than service companies?

Multiple Choice Questions

Use the following code to answer the first three questions

A   3 only
B   2 and 3 only
C   1, 2 and 3
D   1 and 3 only
E   1 and 2 only

- Which of the following direct influences on supply also affect demand?

1   consumer incomes
2   prices of other goods
3   price of the good

- Which of the following is/are correct?

    1   The supply of most products becomes more price elastic with the passage of time.
    2   The demand for most products becomes more price elastic with the passage of time.
    3   Development of a substitute product affects demand but not supply.

- Profit maximisation requires the following conditions

    1   average cost = average revenue
    2   marginal cost = average cost
    3   marginal cost = marginal revenue

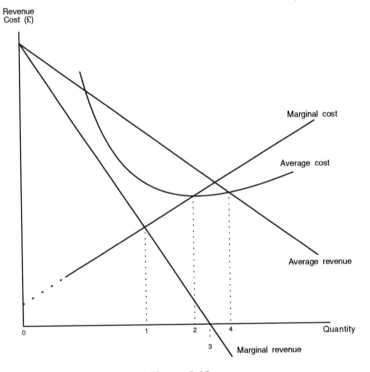

Figure 3.10

The next four questions relate to Figure 3.10.

- The firm maximises revenue at quantity level.

    A   1
    B   2
    C   3
    D   4

- The firm sacrifices profit if it produces above quantity level

  A 1
  B 2
  C 3
  D 4

- The firm operates at the lowest possible cost at quantity level

  A 1
  B 2
  C 3
  D 4

- Assuming that the firm charges a price that enables quantity supplied just to equal demand

  A demand is price elastic at quantity level 1
  B demand is price inelastic at quantity level 2
  C price elasticity of demand is 0 at quantity level 4
  D supply is price inelastic at all quantity levels

- Which of the following is true for the firm which is able to increase output but keep price constant?

  A profit increases, or loss falls as long as output is increased
  B profit or loss is unchanged at each output level
  C profit rises, or loss falls up to the quantity level where marginal cost = average revenue
  D profit rises, or loss falls up to the quantity level where marginal revenue = 0

- In order to achieve economies of scale the firm must produce:

  A at or above its minimum efficient scale of output
  B proportionally more output than it employs inputs
  C at or above the level where marginal cost = average cost
  D proportionally more revenue than it incurs costs

- The firm must be experiencing diminishing marginal returns when its

  A marginal cost is greater than marginal revenue
  B management experiences communication difficulties
  C marginal cost rises with each increment in output
  D average cost is greater than average revenue

4

The structure of the firm

Topic summary

The firm and the entrepreneur

The concept of the entrepreneur was developed to explain and justify profit and to identify profit as the prime motive force for business enterprise. The entrepreneur is the person who contributes the quality of enterprise to economic activity. Enterprise involves a willingness to take risks and to organise other people and production factors in order to achieve production in such a way that profits are made and the other factors rewarded. The concept of the entrepreneur as an individual pursuing and, if successful, being rewarded by profit was ideally suited to the economic conditions of the eighteenth and much of the nineteenth centuries when most business organisations were small and controlled by one or a handful of people. It became apparently less relevant to the twentieth century because

- firms became larger and structured as companies whose ownership and management appeared to have become separated, with success depending more on trained management skills than on the enterprise of owners.
- profits of large companies were distributed to shareholder-owners who had no say in the conduct of the business and who could not contribute business enterprise.
- managerial success appeared to be more concerned with risk avoidance than with risk taking.

In recent years serious attempts have been made to reconcile the basic concept of entrepreneurship with the reality of the large business company taking into account that

- the success of many organisations continues to be associated with the personal qualities of charismatic individuals.
- business success is clearly associated with the ability of senior managers to instil a spirit of entrepreneurship into all levels of management. Without this spirit even the largest firms find it difficult to survive in a competitive world economy.

Entrepreneurship is now defined by many economists as the ability to foresee and organise today for the profitable opportunities that will be available tomorrow. The successful entrepreneurial firm stays ahead of the business field in providing for tomorrow's demand and in making the most efficient use of tomorrow's technological possibilities. Enterprise can thus be shown in all the three areas of economic choice, i.e. in choosing what, how and for whom to produce. It can be displayed at all levels of the business enterprise, not simply by an autocratic head of the organisation. If this modified concept of entrepreneurship is accepted business leadership becomes very much a matter of recruiting, fostering and encouraging individuals and teams throughout the organisation capable of displaying this entrepreneurial capability. Part of this leadership quality will also involve ensuring that those who display entrepreneurial ability share suitably in the resulting profits. You may wish to contrast this with the situation in some large organisations where enterprise is discouraged because unsuccessful risk-taking is heavily penalised and successful risk-taking rarely directly rewarded.

The legal framework of the company

Most business companies are set up under the provisions of the Companies Acts and are limited liability companies with liability limited by shares. They are required to conform to company law. Responsibility for ensuring that company law is observed rests with the Department of Trade and Industry which may, of course, call on the Police to assist in serious criminal cases. The following are among the major features of company structure of most interest to economists.

Share Capital

The total permanent capital of the company is divided into **shares** which are then sold to people or institutions who become shareholders. Each share carries the right to have one vote at shareholder meetings so the more shares a person holds the greater the voting power. Shareholders have no power to intervene in the management of the company but elect a Board of Directors to direct the company on their behalf. There are different classes of shares and these are examined in a later unit. Loan capital can be raised and the form this can take is also examined later.

Directors

The Board of Directors has the duty of directing, i.e. controlling, the company in the interests of its shareholders. They may be full- or part-time and some may represent other sectors of activity of concern to the company. The Board may delegate some of its executive, day-to-day authority to a Managing Director who is always a full-time executive officer of the company. The Board may contain others with managerial duties within the organisation.

Managers

These are employees appointed by or with the authority of the directors and are responsible for day-to-day management. The chief executive, the most senior manager, is usually the General Manager with a seat on the Board of Directors. In small companies this person may also be the Managing Director.

Auditors

These are members of approved professional accountancy bodies and are appointed by the Board but are subject to approval of the shareholders at their Annual General Meeting. Auditors have wide powers of inspecting financial records and must satisfy themselves that the final accounts give a 'true and fair view' of the company's financial affairs or state why they are unable to approve the accounts. Auditors have a duty to protect the interests of shareholders and others, including the government, with an interest in the company's activities.

Basic Assumptions of Company Law

The following appear to be the assumptions at the heart of company law:

- The privilege of limited liability should be available to all organisations willing to follow certain procedures concerning their conduct, who are prepared to accept some degree of financial regulation and submit their final financial accounts to the Department of Trade and indirectly make them available for inspection by anyone wishing to see them. Limited liability is the means whereby people investing in an enterprise are able to limit their maximum possible loss. It arises out of the 'legal fiction' that the company can be given corporate status, i.e. established as an individual body in its own right with an existence entirely separate from its members. These cannot, therefore, be held individually liable for the actions of this separate body, especially if they have taken no part in directing or operating the company. This is in contrast with non-corporate enterprises, such as partnerships. Partners have unlimited liability up to the limit of their own personal possessions for the debts and liabilities of the partnership regardless of any personal responsibility for these.
- In return for the privilege of limited liability companies have to accept a degree of regulation by the State through the Department of Trade which has the duty of protecting shareholders and other members of the public from fraud and financially reckless behaviour. The basis of this protection is a requirement to hold an annual general meeting of shareholders, disclose information and lodge this in a place and form where it may be consulted by members of the public. Since forming a company involves making a contract between those providing and those using finance, company law is seen as a special branch of contract law

in which written contracts are drawn up in certain prescribed forms and must contain certain prescribed information and undertakings. All companies have to produce two important documents, the Memorandum of Association, setting out the name, objectives, share capital, details of founding members and, where relevant, stating that the company is a public company, and the Articles of Association setting out the responsibilities of shareholders, directors and auditors.

- Public companies which are permitted to advertise their shares to the general public and which, therefore, have a greater potential for causing financial harm to members of the general public have greater responsibilities for disclosing information and making this available to people.
- If directors behave with reckless or fraudulent disregard for the interests of those who have entrusted money to the company they may, under certain circumstances, lose the privilege of limited liability. Although many people believe that these conditions are too limited and only likely to occur when the damage has been done, i.e when the company has already become insolvent, this is now established as a principle. It is always possible that the conditions under which the protection of limited liability may be forfeited will be extended in the future.
- There is very little restriction on who may own shares so that these may be held by other companies, by trusts or similar institutions with power to control. This has very wide implications, many of which will become clear in later units. One important aspect to note at this stage is the growth in importance of **institutional shareholders** such as insurance offices and pension funds whose interest in the company is purely financial and who, because of the very large funds they hold, their specialised skills and ability to communicate very rapidly with each other, now tend to wield enormous power over the companies whose shares they hold.

Management structures

Small firms

The organisation of a very small enterprise depends entirely on the abilities and inclinations of the owners and operators. This can remain true as long as the business remains small enough for just one or two people to control. The typical small- to medium-sized family business can thus be said to have a **personal** structure in the sense that the functions and responsibilities of the managers depend very largely on their own interests and abilities. The job and its functions develop around the person of the manager. Communications between managers and between superiors and subordinates depends on personal skills and relationships. They can be good or bad depending on the people concerned. The operation can be small enough for essential information (e.g. a customer's failure to pay according to agreement) to pass to those needing to know without any formal communications procedures.

Large firms

As the firm grows too large for control by one or two people the need for more formal management structures increases. It becomes necessary to create bureaucratic structures in place of earlier informal, personal management relationships. In the bureaucratic structure individuals have to fit the requirements of the office. Successful entrepreneurs, often by nature strong, dominant personalities can find this transition extremely difficult and sometimes impossible. The company risks fragmentation, paralysis or collapse from gross errors of judgement, when a successful entrepreneur is unable to relinquish dominance, delegate or appoint effective managers as opposed to personal servants. Genuine reorganisation is thus essential but one of the most difficult tasks that a successful entrepreneur has to face. Inability to carry it through successfully is one of the most common causes of the failure of previously successful entrepreneurial enterprises.

Types of management structure

There is no right or wrong structure only one that is most appropriate for the particular firm at its particular stage of development. What is right for one period is not necessarily right for the same firm under different conditions. The following are the main types of structure likely to be found in practice. They are not mutually exclusive within the same large enterprise.

- **Hierarchies**
  This is simple and easily understood. In this structure authority and responsibility flow vertically down from a single person at the top through various layers of management to supervision at the actual point of production. There can be several vertical columns of authority and these are frequently based on the various management functions of production, marketing/sales and purchasing. A simplified hierarchy is illustrated in Figure 4.1.

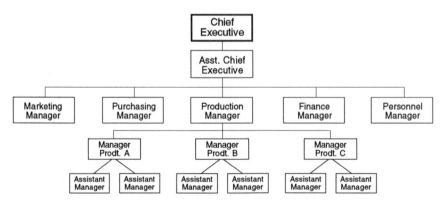

Figure 4.1 A hierarchical structure
Note the possibilities for duplication of work, delay and conflict

- **Divisionalised structures**
  Here the firm's activities are divided into a number of different sectors identified by product or geography or other appropriate division. Within each division there is a hierarchy but divisionalisation enables senior managers to have more direct responsibility for the performance of identifiable parts of the enterprise as they are responsible for all aspects of management for that part. A simplified divisionalised structure is illustrated in Figure 4.2.

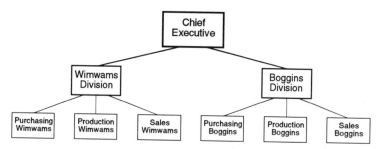

Figure 4.2 Example of divisionalised firm producing two products

- **Matrix structures**
  This is usually more appropriate when managers of varying specialisms are brought together to work on identifiable projects. A management team or series of teams is brought together to combine specialist skills to further clearly identifiable ends. This structure is sometimes used to develop and test potential managers in preparation for more permanent promotion within normal functional departments. The matrix structure is illustrated in Figure 4.3.

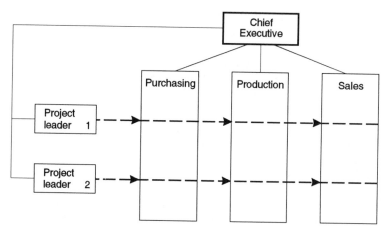

Figure 4.3 Matrix organisation in a firm with two major projects

Planning

One test of an effective structure is its ability to plan. Planning involves:

- Establishing practical and attainable objectives within known constraints.
- Devising appropriate courses of action and assessing the risks involved in each.

Effective management includes the ability to modify or even abandon plans, if their underlying assumptions are no longer valid, without, however, losing sight of the long-term goals of the enterprise.

Discussion and revision questions

- Explain and discuss the view that profit is the just and proper return to successful business enterprise.

- In the 1960s it was often observed that the days of the brilliant individual entrepreneur were over. Business was too specialised and required too much capital for any individual to repeat the successes of Henry Ford or Lord Nuffield. Was this prediction correct? If not how would you explain the continued existence of the successful individual entrepreneur?

- Suggest reasons why the appointment of properly qualified professional auditors is a legal requirement for limited companies but not for partnerships.

- Discuss the benefits and dangers for the community in allowing wide use of the limited company as a form of business structure.

- 'Privatisation has created many millions of new shareholders.'
  'Since 1960 there has been an almost continuous decline in the number and influence of individual shareholders.'
  Suggest explanations for these apparently contradictory statements.

- Explain and discuss the difference between a personal and bureaucratic system of management. Why is the personal structure inappropriate for the large organisation?

- Why are there different kinds of management structures? Suggest reasons why service organisations are often more difficult to manage than manufacturing firms.

Multiple choice questions

- A shareholder in a limited company

  A cannot own more than 51% of that company's shares
  B has just one vote at the Annual General Meeting
  C cannot be another limited company
  D knows the maximum financial loss he/she may suffer if the company fails

The following key applies to the next four questions

  A 1 only is correct
  B 1 and 2 only are correct
  C 3 only is correct
  D 1, 2 and 3 are correct

- All limited companies have to

  1 have a Memorandum and Articles of Association
  2 prepare audited accounts
  3 have directors

- In the case of limited companies

  1 a shareholder, as such, has no right to intervene in the company's management
  2 a shareholder-director is always protected by limited liability
  3 a supplier has more protection than when trading with a partnership

- Only public companies can

  1 advertise their shares for sale to the public
  2 have their shares traded on a stock exchange
  3 continue to increase their share capital without legal limit

- The following characteristics apply to management structures

  1 a divisionalised management avoids the problem of management hierarchies
  2 a matrix management structure loses the advantages of specialised functions
  3 a management hierarchy assumes a vertical flow of authority and responsibility

5

The structure of markets and the conduct and performance of firms

Topic summary

The structure, conduct, performance concept

There is a long tradition in economics that the structure of the market within which a firm operates, influences the conduct of the firm and this, in turn, influences the performance of that firm. To understand the extent to which this concept has dominated economic thinking it is desirable to have a clear idea of what each of these three terms has come to mean. The term **market** denotes any area within which the forces of supply and demand for an identifiable product, or set of products, are able to communicate and interact with each other.

Structure

This is related to the degree of competitiveness held to exist within the market. The starting point for an examination of market structure is usually a consideration of four basic structures: perfect competition, monopolistic competition, monopoly and oligopoly. Each of these is examined in this unit.

Conduct

Much of the analysis of conduct is concerned with product price and the related issue of production output. Since the emphasis is placed on the relationship between the firm and the market, attention is chiefly paid to the extent to which price is determined by market forces beyond the firm's direct control and the extent to which the firm is able to make its own price and output decisions.

Performance

This is related not only to the profit achieved by the firm but also to implications for the economy as a whole. Performance extends to the **efficient** use of resources, efficiency being interpreted as both the effectiveness with which scarce economic resources are used in production — **productive efficiency** — and as the degree to which production meets the requirements of the community — **allocative efficiency**.

Market structures 1, perfect competition

The conditions for perfect competition

This is one extreme of the competitive range. It is an idealised condition under which all market imperfections are completely removed and participants in the market are exposed purely to the interaction of the market forces of supply and demand. It is the economist's equivalent of the pure vacuum in the physical sciences. Study of this extreme ideal can be justified on the grounds that it indicates basic economic tendencies which are manifested under conditions where 'real world' imperfections and frictions are removed. Consequently it helps us to understand the effect of these imperfections and the implications of changing them.

The conditions for perfect competition are well known and, if met, produce this frictionless or 'pure' economic market. They are:

- The market good is perceived as homogeneous, i.e. buyers have no preference for the product of one firm as opposed to another since all units are perceived as having the same qualities.
- Buyers and sellers and potential buyers and sellers are free to enter or leave the market without restriction.
- All participants in the market are influenced only by economic motives, usually interpreted as the maximisation of self-interest, i.e. utility or satisfaction on the part of consumers and profit on the part of business organisations.
- No individual buyer or seller and no group of individuals acting together have sufficient power in the market to influence price by their own behaviour. For this to be the case the size of each buying and selling organisation must be small in relation to the size of the total market.
- There is perfect communication of knowledge and no individual or sector of the market has any advantage over any other in relation to cost or technology.

Profit maximisation

At this stage it is necessary to explain more fully the assumed business motive of **profit maximisation**. This is important because it is also frequently assumed to be the motivating force in other market models and because it has gained some unfavourable social and ethical associations. Profit maximisation does **not** mean the single-minded accumulation of wealth at the expense of the rest of the community nor does it imply the exploitation of the providers of labour (or any other production factor). It simply means the conduct of a business in order to produce a profit which is the largest possible, or suffer a loss which is the lowest possible, under given market conditions.

Profit is defined here in its simplest form as the difference between revenue and cost. It, therefore, represents total revenue (TR) – total cost (TC) and since total revenue = quantity (Q) x average revenue (AR) and total cost = quantity x average cost (AC), we can also see profit in terms of Q(AR – AC). This is useful because average revenue and cost curves are used more frequently than total revenue and cost curves in economic models at the introductory level. Notice that we cannot identify the **amount** of profit or even if the firm is operating at a profit or loss just from marginal revenues and costs. To calculate the amount of profit or loss we need total or average revenue and cost figures. However, to find out whether a change in production is likely to increase or decrease profit (or loss) we do need marginal figures because these, by definition, tell us the effect of changes at the margin.

When related to market structure the maximisation of profit is seen as a short-run condition and is achieved when the **marginal cost of production is equal to the marginal revenue from sales**. This is illustrated in Figures 5.1 and 5.2 for markets where individual firms have to accept the prevailing price (Figure 5.1) and where they are able to influence price through their output decisions (Figure 5.2).

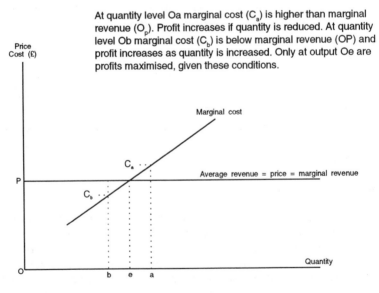

At quantity level Oa marginal cost (C$_a$) is higher than marginal revenue (O$_p$). Profit increases if quantity is reduced. At quantity level Ob marginal cost (C$_b$) is below marginal revenue (OP) and profit increases as quantity is increased. Only at output Oe are profits maximised, given these conditions.

Figure 5.1 Profit maximisation where the firm's output does not influence price

If you do not understand why marginal revenue = unit price in Figure 5.1 or why Or in Figure 5.2 is **not** the unit price you should revise Unit 2.

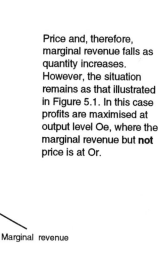

Price and, therefore, marginal revenue falls as quantity increases. However, the situation remains as that illustrated in Figure 5.1. In this case profits are maximised at output level Oe, where the marginal revenue but **not** price is at Or.

Figure 5.2 Profit maximisation where the firm's output influences price

The concept of market equilibrium

In economics, equilibrium is said to exist when two or more interacting forces are perfectly balanced so that there is no pressure to move from the existing situation. A market is in equilibrium when demand and supply intentions are the same. In a market totally free from any outside control equilibrium is achieved by movements of price and quantity. If, at a given price, quantity supplied is greater than quantity demanded price falls and quantity supplied is reduced. If quantity demanded is greater than quantity supplied then price rises and quantity supplied is increased. This adjustment continues until price and quantity levels are achieved where supply and demand are in equilibrium. This can be illustrated by bringing together the demand and supply schedules of Units 2 and 3.

Demand for widgetts in London superstores	
Price per widgett (£)	Quantity per week (number of widgetts)
10	200
9	400
8	600
7	800
6	1000

Supply of widgetts to London superstores	
Price per widgett *(£)*	*Quantity per week* *(number of widgetts)*
5	200
6	400
7	600
8	800
9	1000

If the corresponding demand curve is superimposed on the supply curve — or vice versa — the two intersect at quantity level 700 and unit price £7.50. This result could, of course, be deduced by looking at both schedules. These show that at any price below £7.50 demand is greater than supply. At prices above £7.50 supply is greater than demand. Only at £7.50 are both the same and this, therefore, is the **equilibrium** price. This is shown in Figure 5.3.

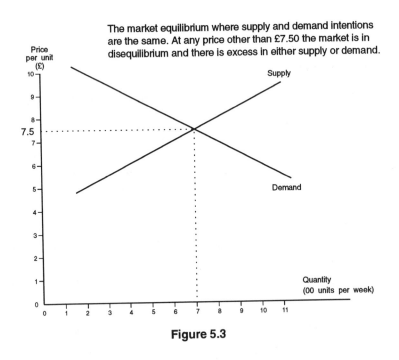

Figure 5.3

The firm in equilibrium

The firm is said to be in equilibrium when there is no pressure to change either price or production quantity level, i.e. when it is achieving its objectives at current prices and quantities. Assuming, as we are at this stage, an objective of profit maximisation the firm will be in equilibrium when its marginal revenue = its marginal cost. As already indicated, however, this can be under conditions where it is making profits or suffering losses. This is illustrated in Figures 5.4 and 5.5.

The best quantity level for the firm is at Oe where marginal cost = marginal revenue. Although this produces a loss because average cost (Oc) is greater than average revenue (Op) the position cannot be improved by any change in quantity level as long as production is continued.
Price
Revenue
Cost (£)
Marginal cost
Average cost
c
p
Price = average revenue = marginal revenue
Quantity sold
O
e

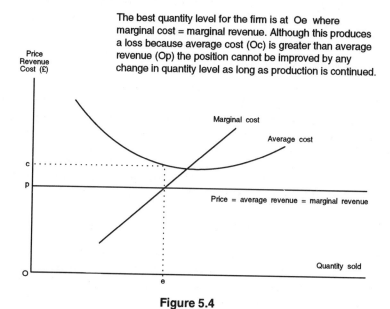

Figure 5.4

The best quantity level for the firm is at Oe where marginal cost = marginal revenue. At any other quantity level profits are reduced. The firm enjoys a profit at Oe equivalent to e(p – c).
Price
Revenue
Cost (£)
Marginal cost
Average cost
p
c
Price = average revenue = marginal revenue
Quantity sold
O
e

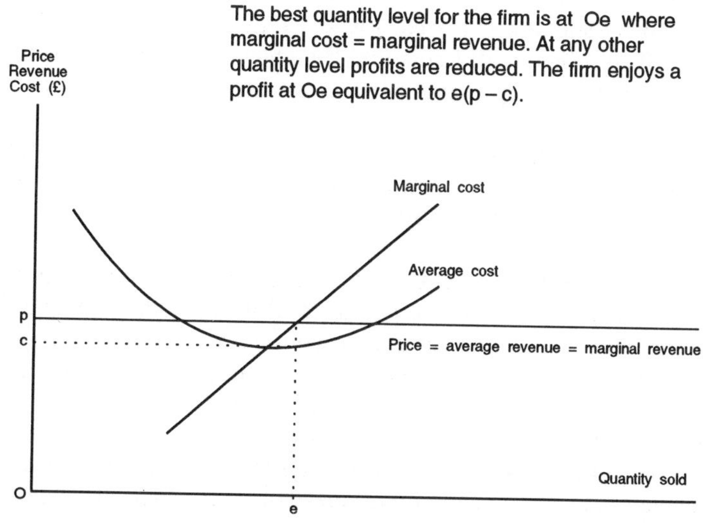

Figure 5.5

Because we are here concerned mainly with perfectly competitive markets where the individual firm cannot influence market price these models show constant price so that price = average = marginal revenue. These figures show that, as long as market and cost conditions remain unchanged the firm cannot do better than produce at the quantity level where marginal cost = marginal revenue. These models assume that the firm has to accept cost conditions and the average cost curve represents its most efficient use of production factors.

The concept of normal profit

If we define cost to include the payments necessary for the use of all production factors we meet the problem of enterprise as a production factor. The traditional view of enterprise sees profit as the corresponding factor payment. This led to the development of the concept of **normal profit** defined in rather vague terms as that amount of profit needed to keep an enterprise in a particular market. Normal profit thus becomes a cost which is included in the average cost curve. This interpretation is necessary for the analysis of equilibrium in the perfectly competitive market.

Market and firm's equilibrium under perfect competition

For this model it is important to remember the condition that there must be unrestricted entry and exit for firms in relation to perfectly competitive markets and also that there is perfect communication of all market knowledge. The process leading to equilibrium is illustrated in Figures 5.6, 5.7 and 5.8.

In Figure 5.6 the firm receives market price Op for as much as it can produce and, at this price it is able to make a profit above the normal represented by the shaded area $q(p - c)$. Given the two conditions just repeated this applies to all firms and the above normal profit attracts an increase in market supply above the existing supply curve (S_o).

In Figure 5.7 supply has increased to S_1 and price fallen to p_1 at which price the firm suffers a loss — the shaded area $q_1(c - p_1)$. This sets up pressure for a reduction in market supply.

In Figure 5.8 market supply has move to S_e, where the firm neither suffers a loss nor earns a profit above the normal as defined in this unit. The produces at level Oq_e where average revenue (price) and average cost are equal $(p_e = c)$. In this equilibrium position the firm has been brought by the market to produce at the level where price = average revenue = average cost (including normal profit) = marginal revenue = marginal cost. It is the equality of marginal cost and price which economists, in the past, have seized on as the basis for arguing that perfect competition offers the community maximum allocative efficiency. This is an issue discussed further in a later unit.

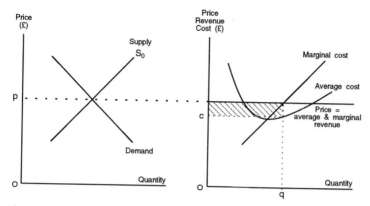

Figure 5.6 The firm making a profit in a perfectly competitive market

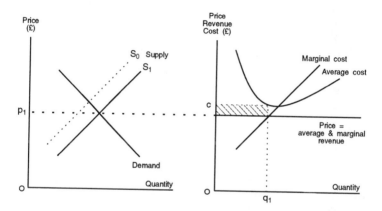

Figure 5.7 The firm suffering a loss following an increase in supply to a perfectly competitive market

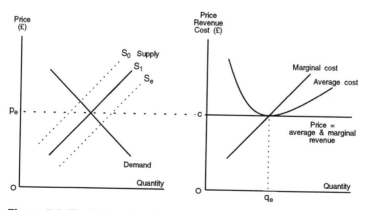

Figure 5.8 The firm and market in equilibrium where profits are normal and there is no pressure to change market supply

The firm in the perfectly competitive market

The welfare and general efficiency implications of perfect competition are examined later. At this stage we consider its implications for the firm. These include

- **Inability to make profits above 'the normal'**
  Business managers argue that this makes it difficult to accumulate capital for investment in new equipment as well as reducing incentives to take risks.

- **Inability to achieve technical superiority over other firms**
  This eliminates incentives to engage in research.

- **Discouragement of marketing**
  There is no point in advertising as all units supplied to the market are perceived as being the same.

- **Instability of prices**
  Any shift in demand causes a swift price reaction and leads to a further set of fluctuations towards equilibrium of the kind illustrated in Figures 5.6 to 5.8.

- **Shifting production levels and product prices**
  This leads to instability in factor markets. Unrestricted entry and exit for product markets can only take place if there is equivalent freedom in factor markets. Modern production tends to be capital intensive and labour specialised. Withdrawal from a market can be costly. There are also strong social and political pressures for stable labour markets. Any return to perfect competition for product markets causes firms to face product price instability and factor price rigidity. Risk taking thus becomes impossibly hazardous.

- **Pressure to produce at the lowest point of the average cost curve**
  This is implied in Figure 5.8. On this basis it is often argued that perfect competition leads to production efficiency. Nevertheless, inability and lack of incentive to undertake technical research, may mean that the cost curve is at a higher level than would be the case if there were faster technical progress.

The general result of the above pressures is to reduce incentives for research, investment in improved production methods and innovation. It is not surprising that firms seek to break away from perfect competition to gain more control over the markets in which they operate.

Market structures 2, monopoly

The opposite extreme from perfect competition is monopoly which, in its strictest form is defined as a market where there is only **one** supplier. The demand curve of the monopolist is thus the market demand curve which we can take as being downward sloping. Continuing the assumption of profit maximising behaviour the familiar model of monopoly is shown in Figure 5.9.

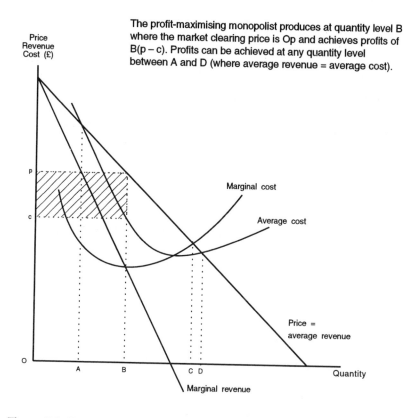

The profit-maximising monopolist produces at quantity level B where the market clearing price is Op and achieves profits of B(p – c). Profits can be achieved at any quantity level between A and D (where average revenue = average cost).

Figure 5.9 The monopoly model where the firm's demand curve is the market demand curve

This suggests that profits above the normal can be achieved over a wide range of quantities and prices — between A and D in Figure 5.9 — and that profits are maximised at quantity level B where marginal revenue = marginal cost.

The welfare implications of monopoly and near monopoly are examined in a later unit but note here that economists have argued that monopoly leads to lower output and higher prices than would be achieved under perfect competition. This is based on an assumption that firms under perfect competition would produce at quantity level C, where marginal cost = price. However, there is a counter argument that the ability to make profits permits and encourages firms to engage in technical research and capital investment and so reduce costs. This, combined with economies of scale resulting from the replacement of many small firms by one large firm makes it likely, that the monopolist's average cost curve is below the aggregate cost curve of firms under perfect competition. It becomes possible, therefore, to argue that monopoly price may be lower and output higher than under perfect competition.

The debate over the conduct of the monopolist as opposed to that of perfectly competitive firms thus shifts from profits to costs. The question is whether increased market power and ability to make profits lead to greater cost efficiency or whether freedom from the pressures of competition leads to lack of innovation and failure to invest and reduce costs. This is not a question that can be answered by theoretical analysis. It requires observation of the actual behaviour of firms and this issue will also be explored in a later unit.

Market structures 3, monopolistic competition

In between the extremes of perfect competition and monopoly a number of models of market structure have been developed and one of these is termed **monopolistic** competition because it contains features of both the extreme conditions. The main conditions for monopolistic competition are:

- Suppliers are able to persuade buyers that there are differences between the products of different suppliers who are likely to engage in branding and advertising to emphasise the claimed unique features of each brand and thus to establish a monopoly over supply of the particular brand even though each brand is perceived as a close substitute for its rivals.
- There remain largely unrestricted entry to and exit from the product market.
- Suppliers and buyers are not powerful enough to influence market price of the class of product as a whole though they can set their own brand prices within the market's price expectations.
- Motives remain firmly economic and for suppliers this means an assumption of profit-maximising behaviour.
- Communications are not perfect but they are still good. No one firm is able to achieve clear superiority in technology or marketing skills but not all knowledge is fully shared throughout the market.

Given these conditions the situation where the firm is in equilibrium in this market is illustrated in Figure 5.10.

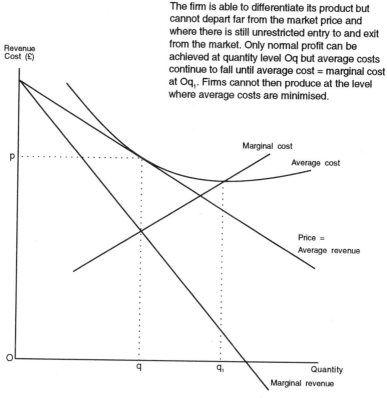

The firm is able to differentiate its product but cannot depart far from the market price and where there is still unrestricted entry to and exit from the market. Only normal profit can be achieved at quantity level Oq but average costs continue to fall until average cost = marginal cost at Oq_1. Firms cannot then produce at the level where average costs are minimised.

Figure 5.10 Monopolistic competition

Market structures 4, oligopoly

Oligopoly is the term given to a market in which supply is dominated by a few, usually very large, companies. The special case of domination by two companies only is called duopoly. Unlike the other market structures there is no single universally accepted model of oligopoly. One model, frequently associated with this market, explains the feature well recognised in non-inflationary times that the product price tends to remain constant in spite of frequent changes in raw material and other input prices. For reasons that are obvious when you look at Figure 5.11 this is called the kinked demand curve model. The explanation for the kink is the assumption that all the supplying firms tend to charge the same price. If any single supplier tries to raise the price the others do not follow. If an individual supplier reduces price the others do follow so that the demand curve is more price sensitive above the ruling price than below. The following table illustrates this situation.

1	2	3	4 (Δ3 ÷ Δ2)
Price per unit (£)	*Quantity (units per time period)*	*Total Revenue (£)*	*Marginal Revenue (£)*
12	10	120	
			10
11	20	220	
			8
10	30	300	(7) or (4)
			2
8	40	320	
			− 2
6	50	300	
			− 6
4	60	240	

This table is the basis for Figure 5.11.

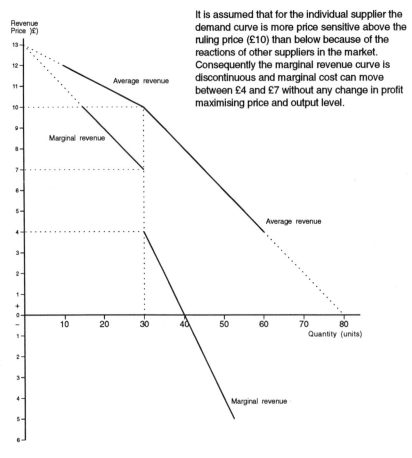

It is assumed that for the individual supplier the demand curve is more price sensitive above the ruling price (£10) than below because of the reactions of other suppliers in the market. Consequently the marginal revenue curve is discontinuous and marginal cost can move between £4 and £7 without any change in profit maximising price and output level.

Figure 5.11 The kinked demand curve

Here the price tends to 'stick' at £10. Above this price each £1 price change produces a quantity change of 10 units. Below, a £1 change only produces a quantity change of 5 units so that it takes a £2 movement in price to produce a 10 unit quantity movement. The marginal revenue changes by £2 (double the price-average revenue change) above the sticky price but by £4 (again double the price-average revenue change) below it. If you calculate the marginal revenue for the quantity level of 30 units where the price is £10 you will see that it is £7 if you measure down from the upper part of the curve or £4 if you extend upwards from the lower part of the curve. This gives a discontinuity between £7 and £4. Since profit maximisation requires marginal revenue to equal marginal cost this means that marginal cost can fluctuate between £7 and £4 without putting any pressure on firms to change their prices or output levels.

This model only explains one feature of oligopolistic behaviour given certain market conditions (no price inflation and products that are close substitutes). Under conditions of severe price inflation when buyers are anticipating price rises, the pricing behaviour is likely to be reversed — any individual movement to raise price will be followed while an individual attempt to reduce price or failure to follow a rise, may be ignored in the belief that the deviation will only be very short-lived.

The challenge to profit maximisation

The general assumption that firms seek to maximise profits has been challenged on a number of grounds including

- The recognition that firms with significant market power do not need to **maximise** profits to survive. They can make adequate profits over a fairly wide range of output and prices. It is possible, therefore, that they could pursue other objectives and still survive in the long term.
- The possibility that, in practice, managers are able to maintain sufficient independence from the ultimate control of shareholders that they can pursue objectives that they find rewarding and do not seek to maximise the shareholders' interests — assumed to be profit — as long as they achieve **sufficient** profit to avoid a shareholder revolt.
- Suggestions that firms' actual conduct and behaviour does not accord with the predictions based on assumptions of profit maximisation. In particular it is suggested that firms do frequently raise prices in response to an increase in fixed costs — conduct consistent with seeking a particular level or percentage of profit but not consistent with profit maximisation. There is also little evidence that advertising expenditure is set at profit-maximising levels.
- The argument that given the conditions of uncertainty and imperfect information under which managerial decisions have to be made, firms cannot pursue a policy of profit maximisation if they wished to do so.

The search for an alternative to profit maximisation

If there is any suggestion that profit maximisation should be abandoned as the objective of business firms an alternative has to be put forward and various possibilities have been raised.

Revenue maximisation

One of the earliest of the alternative theories was that firms sought to pursue maximum sales revenue once a satisfactory level of profit was achieved, this level being defined as that needed to retain the support of shareholders and financial institutions. Some consequences of this assumption are illustrated in Figure 5.12.

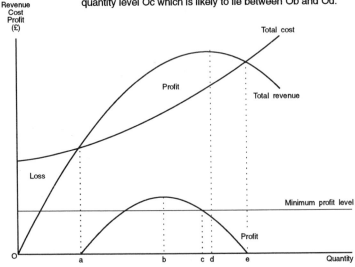

The model assume that the firm seeks to maximise revenue subject to achieve a minimum profit. The firm can make some profit between the two break points Oa and Oe. Profit is maximised at Ob and revenue is maximised at the higher quantity level of Od. The minimum profit is achieved at quantity level Oc which is likely to lie between Ob and Od.

Figure 5.12 The revenue maximising model

In order to achieve greater clarity and precision this model uses total revenue and cost curves. The firm is able operate profitably at any quantity level between Oa and Oe, thus raising the possibility of non-profit maximising behaviour. If the firm did seek to maximise profits it would seek to produce at quantity level Ob — the peak of the profits curve. If it felt free to maximise revenue without any effective profit constraint it could produce at quantity level Od — the peak of the total revenue curve. If, however, there is an effective profit constraint preventing the firm from seeking maximum revenue it would produce at the highest quantity level possible, subject to achieving the required level of profit. In Figure 5.12 this is quantity Oc.

Notice that Od and Oc are both at higher levels than Ob. Only if the minimum profit was established at the maximum possible level of profits would Oc and Ob occur at the same point. For Od and Ob to come together marginal cost would have to be zero—an unlikely situation for most firms. Our conclusion, therefore, is that a firm behaving as this model suggests would produce at a higher output level and, by implication, sell its product at a lower price than a firm seeking to maximise profits.

An increase in fixed costs would lead to an increase in total costs, reduce the area of profit between total revenue and cost and reduce the profit curve. If you draw in a second profit curve a little below the one shown in Figure 5.12 and roughly parallel to it you will see that minimum profit can only be maintained by reducing the quantity produced and, by implication, raising the price. Assuming the normal downward sloping demand curve likely to be faced by a large firm enjoying a high degree of market power, any reduction in output will force the firm to move up the demand curve, i.e. charge a higher price in order to avoid stock shortages or excesses.

Such a firm, with its preference for revenue, is also likely to have a preference for activities which tend to increase revenue. One of the most important of these will be advertising. A revenue-maximising firm can be expected to spend more on advertising than could be justified if it was trying to maximise profits.

Managerial utility maximisation

Another suggestion put forward to explain the behaviour of large firms is that controlling managers will seek to maximise their own utility and that this is likely to include

- **Discretionary profit**
  This is defined as profit above the minimum needed to satisfy shareholders and financial institutions. Managers continue to have a preference for profit because this is highly regarded by fellow managers and it allows the manager to have a higher spending budget and generally confers increased prestige and status.

- **Staff growth**
  Managers wish to increase the number of people employed since the more people managed the higher their status, salary, etc.

- **Emoluments** or **perks**
  The larger the unit managed the larger the company car, travel and other visible signs of status and success.

This managerial utility leads to expenditure which reduces the share of profit going to shareholders and represents a breach of the managerial duty to pursue the interests of shareholder. It is a consequence of loss of control over managerial actions by the representatives of the shareholders. It has been argued, therefore, that this loss together with profit-maximising behaviour can be restored by organisational changes within the firm, in particular by linking managerial performance more directly to the achievement of profit.

The behavioural theory of the firm

This is a major challenge to conventional analysis of business conduct and performance. The theory sees the firm as a coalition of potentially conflicting interest groups (customers, managers, shareholders) which nevertheless have a common interest in the continued survival of the firm. This perception leads to the belief that the coalition is likely to have several goals which are pursued sequentially. The goals originally suggested were sales, market share, profit, production (continuity and professional standards) and inventories (having sufficient stocks to satisfy all likely buyer demands) but others may be added or substituted. Attention is paid to the decision-making processes within the firm and four main behavioural concepts governing these are identified. These are

- **Quasi resolution of conflict**
  No single goal satisfies the aspirations of all members of the coalition and there will remain some conflict of interest (such as sales volume at the expense of profit) but compromises will be made in order to achieve a sufficient degree of satisfaction to keep the coalition together.

- **Uncertainty avoidance**
  The greater the uncertainty the more difficult decision making becomes so managers seek to reduce this by controlling both the external and internal environment in which the firm operates, e.g. by advertising, collusion with fellow oligopolists and by sticking to company procedures and rules.

- **Problemistic search**
  New solutions to problems are only sought when the old solution fails, a problem being defined as anything that threatens the stability of the coalition, e.g. falling sales, profits, dissatisfied customers, disruptions to production. When search is undertaken it is directed towards finding the nearest **satisfactory** and not the **best possible** solution. These behavioural assumptions can be contrasted with **maximising** objectives which imply constant search activity — to find the best possible solution to all problems.

- **Organisational learning**
  A new solution becomes part of the organisation's rules of conduct to guide future managerial decisions — until it fails to solve problems.

This concept also suggests that goals and expected achievement levels are established and modified in the light of managers' own experience, their perceptions of the experience of other firms and the success with which earlier goals were achieved.

These concepts cast some light on the managerial processes and they offer an analytical framework for understanding behaviour in those public sector organisations where profit can never be an overriding objective. On the other hand behavioural theory has some significant limitations. It describes what firms appear to be doing but has little to say about what they should be doing in order to achieve efficiency of both technical performance and allocation. Enterprise and initiative appear to be ignored. Day-to-day survival appears to be the main underlying aim of everyone connected with the firm. Some observers have commented that if behavioural theory does accurately describe the conduct of large business firms in the USA and Western Europe in the 1960s and early 1970s then it goes a long way to explain their difficulties when faced with increasing world competition in the mid 1970s and 1980s. It might also help to account for the British public's disenchantment with the public sector in the 1970s which, in turn, helped to bring about the political changes of the 1980s.

You may have noticed that growth in some form or other is a feature of the alternative theories of the firm. Growth, in fact, is such an important issue that it is the main topic examined in the next unit.

Discussion and revision questions

- Discuss different possible ways for evaluating the performance of firms in a particular market.

- In a market approximating to perfect competition would you expect prices to be stable or unstable? Justify your answer.

- 'Modern industrial society with its ideals of property ownership and stable, protected employment, cannot tolerate the uncertainties and instabilities of perfect competition.' Explain and discuss this statement.

- 'Perfect competition is a market which is neither perfect nor competitive.' Explain and discuss this statement.

- 'It is not so much monopoly profits that require pubic scrutiny but monopoly costs.' How far is this a justifiable comment?

- On what grounds might a business manager defend a monopoly against charges that it operates against the public interest?

- How may competition be monopolistic?

- Discuss the proposition that perfect competition leads inevitably to monopolistic competition which, equally inevitably, leads to oligopoly.

- 'The kinked demand curve model is not a complete model of oligopoly.' Why not?

- The following is the price-quantity schedule for product X. What would you expect to be the market price of X, assuming an oligopolistic market?

Price per unit (£)	Quantity (units per time period)
8.50	200
9.00	190
9.50	180
10.00	170
10.50	160
11.00	140
11.50	120
12.00	100

- Add a marginal revenue table to this schedule and draw a diagram showing the average and marginal revenue curves.

- Why have there been repeated attempts to replace the assumption of profit maximisation by completely different theories to explain business behaviour?

- How far is it true to say that most of the criticisms levelled at profit maximisation apply equally to revenue maximisation subject to achieving a minimum profit?

- 'Firms seeking revenue maximisation are more likely to achieve efficiency than those seeking profit maximisation.' How far would you agree with this statement?

- Discuss the comment that 'The strength of the behavioural theory of the firm lies in its descriptive accuracy but this is also its weakness.'

Multiple choice questions

The key below applies to the following five questions

A 1 only is correct
B 1 and 2 only are correct
C 3 only is correct
D 1, 2 and 3 are correct

- The following are essential characteristics of suppliers to a perfectly competitive market

  1 firms are small in relation to the size of the market
  2 all firms face the same input costs
  3 firms can enter or leave the market as they wish

- When a perfectly competitive market is in equilibrium

  1 firms cannot achieve supernormal profits
  2 firm's marginal costs are equal to average costs
  3 market demand is fully satisfied

- Under conditions of monopolistic competition

  1 only the most efficient firms can achieve supernormal profits
  2 all firms charge the same price
  3 firms may enter or leave the market as they choose

- The kinked demand curve model explains the tendency for prices of oligopolists to remain constant in spite of fluctuating costs on the basis of the individual firm's inability to

  1 raise price above those of competitors without losing market share
  2 achieve supernormal profit
  3 pass on cost increases to buyers

- The behavioural theory of the firm makes the following assumptions about the decision-making behaviour of the organisation

  1 conflict between decision makers cannot be totally resolved
  2 firms will seek to control the environment in which they operate
  3 firms will seek to achieve satisfactory rather than the best possible solutions to problems

- Advertising is least likely in markets which approximate to

  A perfect competition
  B monopolistic competition
  C oligopoly
  D monopoly

- Technical research and innovation are least likely in markets which approximate to

  A perfect competition
  B monopolistic competition
  C oligopoly
  D monopoly

The following diagram which shows the revenue and cost curves of a firm which is a major supplier to its market relates to the next three questions. Assume that the firm's costs include normal profit.

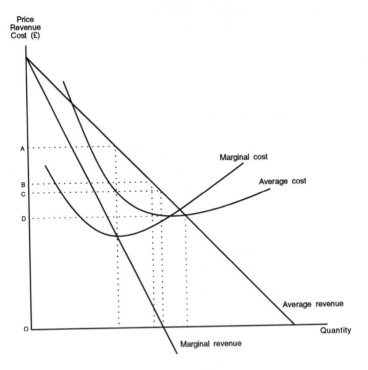

Figure 5.13

- The firm's revenue is maximised at price

  A OA
  B OB
  C OC
  D OD

- The firm's profit is maximised at price

  A OA
  B OB
  C OC
  D OD

- The firm's profitable output is maximised at price

  A OA
  B OB
  C OC
  D OD

6
Business growth

Topic summary

The pressures for growth

It is difficult not to be aware that there are many very large business organisations and most of these continue to grow even larger. There must clearly be some strong pressures to account for this. Among the most important appear to be the following.

Cost conditions

A common explanation is based on **economies of scale**. These are present when growth enables a firm to produce at a reduced average total cost. These economies are either pecuniary or real.

Pecuniary economies relate to money costs only. They can arise when the large firm uses its buying power in the market to obtain inputs at a lower price than smaller competitors can secure or when it uses its power as a monopoly or dominant seller to force distributors to accept reduced trade discounts. The ability to achieve these cost savings displays superior market power rather than superior efficiency in the use of resources.

Real economies occur when growth enables the firm to increase its output by a larger percentage than the increase in factor inputs, e.g. when a 10% increase in the use of land, labour and capital produces a 15% increase in production output. This is a real economy because it demonstrates efficient use of scarce resources and makes possible genuine economic growth.

Real economies from an increased scale of production can arise through:

- Larger, more efficient and, often technically more advanced equipment. Even having more equipment can give the larger firm more flexibility and ability to cope with production problems. The existence of, say, spare machine capacity enables the firm to cope with breakdowns and with temporarily increased demands on production more easily than the small firm which may be fully using all its equipment.

- The ability to make full use of specialist managers in such activities as marketing, purchasing, personnel and finance. Managers in smaller organisations often have to operate across several specialities and are unlikely to be equally competent in all of them.
- Entry to the full range of financial services in ways denied to smaller organisations. Raising capital by public share issue is an expensive process and only worthwhile for large sums. Coping with several different currencies can be expensive and time consuming for small firms whereas large firms are often able to maintain several different foreign currency accounts and can readily trade in all the main currencies.
- Market power can bring real as well as pecuniary advantages. Manufacturers which have already shown the ability to succeed in one product market find it easier to convince store buyers that their new product lines should be stocked, especially when they undertake to support these with heavy advertising and other forms of promotion. Advertising itself offers substantial economies of scale. The multinational, able to spend many thousands of pounds on a TV cartoon commercial with different language sound tracks, can show this in a dozen or more countries at peak viewing time and achieve an exposure cost (cost per exposure to each potential buyer) far lower than the small firm only able to spend a few hundred pounds for advertising on local radio.

Limitations to scale economies

Nevertheless economies of scale cannot be a complete explanation for business growth because these tend to diminish as size increases. There is substantial evidence to indicate that the typical long-run, average cost curve for the business organisation is L-shaped. The main advantages from scale economies come in the early stages of growth. Depending on the production methods employed and the mix of fixed and variable costs the decline in average total costs may be steep or gentle but in either case there will come a stage where further reductions in average cost will be very small in relation to the size increase required for their achievement. This stage is usually referred to as the **minimum efficient scale of output (MES)** and this is illustrated in Figure 6.1.

You will see here that the output differences between Oq_1 and Oq_2, and Oq_2 and Oq_3 are the same but the cost reduction, from Oc_1 to Oc_2 is much greater than from Oc_2 to Oc_3. For this cost curve, therefore, the minimum efficient scale is in the region of output level Q^*. Above this level further average cost savings may achieved but will not bring significant market advantages and may easily be more than outweighed by superior marketing skills. Nevertheless, there are many industries which contain firms far larger than their MES so that their size cannot be explained purely be economies of scale. Further explanations must be sought.

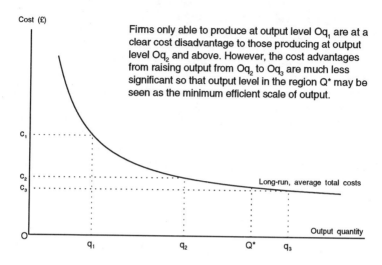

Figure 6.1 The minimum efficient scale (MES) of output

Market power

Size not only brings marketing economies it also brings market power and a reduction in competition. To be known as a brand leader for a well-known consumer product brings considerable benefits, not only in smoothing the launch of new products but also in gaining shelf space for existing products. Large stores tend to allocate shelf space according to market share so that brand leaders enjoy the largest allocation. Consequently they have the most to gain from impulse buying which reinforces their dominance. Challengers must spend proportionally more on promotions to have much chance of making inroads into the dominant brand's share of the market.

Managerial preferences

The outline of managerial objectives in the previous unit recognised the importance of growth to managerial satisfaction. For senior managers movement from one firm to another is not always easy. Consequently the main route to increased salary, status and perks is by expanding the present position, i.e. by pressing for expansion even where this may be at the expense of some profit. Growth is the most obvious, outward sign of business success and may help to create a reputation outside the company and lead to the possibility of movement.

The capital market

Although growth can be at the expense of profitability the modern capital market, from time to time appears to share with managers the same belief that growth is synonymous with success. Perhaps this is because it too is dominated by the professional managers of the financial institutions who are judged largely by their achievements in expanding the capital value of the funds they manage. The rapid expansion of a relatively few fashionable firms in the 1980s, was aided by the favour of investment managers who chased up their share values which in turn inflated the value of the funds they managed. Many of these bubbles burst in 1989–91 to show how financially fragile were some of the foundations on which over-rapid growth had been built. Stockbrokers and merchant banks have everything to gain from merger, take-overs and any kind of activity which encourages share sales. They have nothing to gain from periods of stable profitability. It has to be doubted whether the present structure and organisation of the capital market are in the best long-term interests either of business companies or their shareholders.

Types of growth

Business growth is usually said to be either **internal** or **external**. Internal growth is achieved by expanding the activities of the firm, for example, by opening new stores, building new factories, breaking into new markets with new products, expanding market share with increased sales. This type of growth requires the firm to recruit new staff who must either be trained or poached from competitors. Market share has to be won from competition and there is the constant uncertainty that projections made to justify the expansion will not, in practice, be realised. As the firm becomes larger this kind of growth becomes progressively more difficult and senior managers tend to become increasingly attracted by the external route.

External growth is achieved by merger and take-over. In practical terms there is little difference between the two as there is always one dominant partner following any merger. Most text books imply that merger involves the swallowing up of company A in its entirety by company B either to create an expanded B or a new organisation — C. However, in the past two decades the majority of mergers have involved arrangements whereby company A has taken over a subsidiary of company B to the benefit of both A and B. The sale allows A to expand in an area where it is already strong or where it has the resources for profitable development, whereas B divests itself of an activity which does not fit easily into its own strategic development plan and gains finance for expanding in the direction it wishes to follow. For the rest of this unit the general term merger is used in relation to all arrangements in which one company acquires another as a going concern whether it is technically a full or part merger or take over. Mergers can be horizontal, vertical or conglomerate.

- **Horizontal mergers**
These involve expansion in the same industry at the same stage of the production cycle, e.g. when one retail chain acquires another chain in the same product range, or one motor manufacturer acquires another as when Ford acquired Jaguar. The attractions of this type of growth are clear. The number of competing firms is reduced; the company is expanding in the area of its own specialised interests and it may be able to increase productivity by eliminating overlapping services such as transport and making fuller use of available resources.

- **Vertical mergers**
These refer to movement along the production cycle in its existing industry either forwards, e.g. manufacturing into distribution, or backwards, e.g. distribution into manufacturing. This movement may be to gain greater control over the production cycle by ensuring access to markets through distributors or ensuring supplies of goods. In general, however, vertical mergers tend to be less successful than horizontal, partly because the different stages of production appear to require different styles of management. The techniques of manufacturing management do not transfer well to distribution and few distribution companies seem able to make a success of manufacturing. Another major problem is that the most efficient sizes of operation tend to be different in the different stages of production so that the vertically integrated firm tends to suffer from over or under capacity and it cannot expect rival firms to assist it by absorbing surplus production or supplying shortfalls. Moreover, manufacturers frequently expect their distribution outlets to specialise in their own products so that they then suffer because they cannot provide buyers with the range of choice demanded by the market.

- **Conglomerate mergers**
These are the least successful because they cut across the fundamental economic principle of specialisation. They involve mergers between companies operating in different industries and often at different stages of the production cycle. The usual justification for conglomerate or diversified merger is to gain additional security from interests in different activities so that the company is not at the mercy of cycles in just one industry. Companies that face problems in their core industry sometimes seek protection through diversification. Imperial Group, formerly Imperial Tobacco, facing declining tobacco sales, took this route but, in the process, suffered a decline in profitability and itself became a takeover target. It fell to Hanson which divested the Group of most of its non-tobacco interests and expanded its tobacco sales overseas.

Some implications of growth

Growth may strengthen or weaken a firm. It will certainly put strains on its finances and management structure and is likely to change its character.

Financial strains

Growth, whether internal or external requires finance. There are three sources of finance: retained profit, borrowings or additional 'owners capital' which for companies means share capital also known as equity.

- **Retained profit**
  The more profit is used to finance growth the less it is available to make payments to shareholders. Failure to satisfy shareholders can threaten the existence of the company. For family companies there may be dissatisfied members of the family who will sell their shares to competitors. Shareholders of larger public companies with a low dividend payment record are also likely to sell and so depress the share price. The company's market value (share price x number of shares) may under-value its asset or balance sheet value (value of all assets) or its true value in terms of capacity to make future profits, and the company will become vulnerable to take over.

- **Borrowing**
  Borrowing can seem attractive in periods of rising sales and profits and relatively low interest rates. If a company can borrow at an interest rate of 10% and achieve a profit return of 20% the advantages are obvious. However, if conditions change the interest charge may rise to 15% and the profit rate drop to 12% or lower and then the company is in serious financial trouble and, at best, may have to sell potentially valuable physical assets to reduce its debt. A company with a high ratio of debt to equity is said to be **highly geared**. Financial text books have suggested that retail companies can be highly geared more safely than manufacturing companies because they can always sell stock and hold back on purchases to reduce debt. This is probably true for a grocery-based supermarket but it clearly did not apply to the speciality chains such as Tie Rack, Sock Shop and Next, which plunged into serious problems in the late 1980s and early 1990s when all retail sales fell, especially in the non-essential, non-food areas.

- **Additional equity**
  Increasing the number of shares **dilutes** the value of existing shares because profits have to be more thinly distributed and dividends can only be maintained if profits rise in greater proportion than the increase in shares. For a small family-controlled company growth by increasing equity often means a loss of family control. The new shares are likely to be bought by financial institutions which insist on representation on the Board of Directors and may also insist on managerial changes. In the

case of large public companies the Stock Exchange insists that new shares are first offered to existing shareholders through a **rights issue** in which shareholders are offered, say one new share for every n old shares held. The dominant shareholders are likely to be financial institutions who tend to dislike such issues because they may not wish to have additional shares in that company but also do not wish to ignore the rights as this will depress the share price and the value of their current holding. In a strongly rising market rights issues are readily acceptable but in a weak market they become difficult and expensive.

Given the financial problems involved it may seem strange that so many mergers take place but the capital market exists to find solutions to these problems and it will always find finance for companies it believes capable of generating profits.

Management strains

A growing firm requires additional managers. A firm growing by merger acquires managerial teams which have to be restructured, often reduced in size and the survivors integrated into the main company team. All this takes a certain amount of time and a company trying to grow too quickly may suffer as much from managerial as from financial pressures. Recent business history suggests that the most vulnerable companies are those whose growth is inspired by strong, charismatic leaders who have failed to strengthen their corporate management structures to meet the strains of large-scale operation but have simply expanded the structures which first carried them to success. Such firms can collapse even more quickly than they grew. The successful firm is the one able to make the difficult transition from being an extension of the entrepreneural individual to a corporation in which groups of specialist managers are able to coordinate their efforts to achieve clearly expressed and carefully formulated, practical objectives. Many companies which have made this transition successfully still remain under the ultimate control of a dominant family. Recent studies suggest that these firms face special managerial strains. Those that overcome them and succeed in reconciling family interests with those of business efficiency include some of the most successful multinational enterprises but many do not and fewer than one in five manage to survive the second generation of family control.

Small firms

Not all firms grow large. Not all business owners are ambitious to control giant multinational enterprises. Many are content to earn what they perceive as a satisfactory income and to operate on a local basis.

Definition and importance of small firms

It is not possible to define a small firm in terms of a precise measure of capital or labour employed. Changing technology and money values quickly make any such attempt out of date. The essential features, however, are:

- genuine independence of any larger concern.
- small size in relation to the market in which it operates.
- subject to the personal day-to-day management (not just overall control) of its owners.

The great majority of business firms in the United Kingdom are small in these terms. Quite apart from the thousands of sole traders and other non-corporate firms at least three out of four companies are family controlled and most (though not all) of these are small. Around a quarter of the workforce is employed in small firms and these produce over one fifth of all goods and services in the United Kingdom. To the economy as a whole these firms provide flexibility and innovation. They can adapt quickly to technical change and many cling to life with great tenacity under conditions where large firms would simply liquidate their operations. The collapse of a small firm usually means heavy loss of income and savings for the owner as well as any workers employed. New activities such as microcomputer manufacturing and software production were initially developed by small firms. Later some of these became large or were absorbed by large companies.

Reasons for survival of the small firm sector

Although the average life expectancy of the small firm is low there are always likely to be small firms.

- The cost structure of many activities is such that the minimum efficient scale of output is small in relation to the size of the market. Where there are no substantial technical economies of scale any economies there might be can be balanced by a simple and informal administrative and communication structure. Consequently the large firm has no cost advantages over the small and may face the prospect of diseconomies of scale so that the long-run, average total cost curve may incline more towards the U–than the L–shape. Many service activities are of this kind. Few manufacturers of electrical household goods attempt to provide local maintenance and repair services. Most prefer to franchise these to small local firms.
- Where markets are small the suppliers must also be small. Rising living standards are creating more specialised markets side by side with mass markets. We are all familiar with mass produced, 'cheddar cheese' as sold in the superstore chains. A number of small suppliers have built up significant markets in genuine country cheeses. Small shops still prosper in towns too small to attract the superstore chains.

- Large firms are often ready to contract out work which they know they cannot carry out profitably. In this way they retain their customers and make some profit while providing work for firms small enough to handle it effectively.
- Small, family-owned firms are often more resilient than larger corporations in the face of difficult market conditions. Owners face personal disaster if they fail and the prospect of this spurs people to search for ways to survive.
- The ease of starting a small business ensures that there will always be some people willing to take the risks involved. Periods of recession tend to increase the numbers starting new ventures. If there is actual or potential unemployment looming in the future the opportunity cost of embarking on self-employment is reduced and more people are prepared to face this cost.
- Many people find employment in a large organisation a frustrating experience, especially if they are innovators and want to experiment with new ideas. Most of those who have real faith in a new production process or product are likely to want to test it through their own efforts and face failure in the hope of reaping the rewards of success.

Weaknesses of small firms

Although there will always be small firms the majority face a very brief life span. Fewer than half of all new enterprises survive into the second year and many of the survivors provide only a very small income for their owners. The most common reasons for failure are:

- Insufficient finance to obtain necessary equipment, to bridge the often long time-gap between incurring production costs and receiving payments from buyers or to hire people with the necessary level of skill. Most new business owners underestimate the amount of finance needed in the crucial first year.
- Inadequate or unrealistic market research, often combined with unwillingness to admit that demand for the product is never going to be sufficient to maintain a profitable level of sales. This also tends to be combined with an inability, through lack of finance or knowledge, to foster latent demand or to adapt the product to the demands of the market place. A common fault of those convinced of the intrinsic worth of their products is a failure to pay attention to packaging and presentation.
- Lack of the necessary management skills to cope with the varied demands of running a business. Previous employment in a large firm leaves many with skills in one or two specialist areas but almost total ignorance of other areas of management. The producer tends to be weak on financial management and administration while the ex-accountant or financial manager can have inadequate knowledge of marketing or lack ability to manage production.

Discussion and revision questions

- By the end of the 1980s there was widespread recognition that in the case of many large companies 'the sum of the parts was more valuable than the whole'.
  Suggest reasons why such companies had grown to the extent that they were in this condition.

- Under what conditions is growth likely to produce (a) economies of scale, (b) diseconomies of scale?

- Explain the significance of the Minimum Efficient Scale of production to the growth of firms.

- Explain the preference for growth by merger and take-over in modern economies.

- 'Successful companies often suffer from growing pains and success can be as dangerous as failure for the relatively new enterprise.'
  Explain and discuss this statement.

- Why is it difficult to define 'small firm' in terms of capital or labour employed? How would you distinguish a small from a large firm?

- In view of the obvious risks of failure why do so many people each year start up new enterprises? How might they reduce their own personal risks?

Multiple choice questions

The key below applies to the following five questions

A   1 only is correct
B   1 and 2 only are correct
C   3 only is correct
D   1, 2 and 3 are correct

- Real economies of scale exist when firms

  1   increase output in greater proportion than they increase inputs
  2   increase sales turnover by reducing price
  3   have sufficient market power to obtain price concessions from suppliers

- Rapid growth weakens a firm when

  1   the value of its shares is diluted
  2   it becomes very highly geared
  3   its management becomes specialised

- Vertical integration tends to be less successful than horizontal integration for manufacturing companies because

  1 it increases the number of competing suppliers selling to manufacturers
  2 by introducing transfer pricing it raises total production costs
  3 optimum production levels often differ in the different sectors of production

- To be classed as a small firm an enterprise should

  1 have a relatively small share of its product market
  2 be independent of any other organisation
  3 be structured as a sole proprietor or partnership

- The proportion of service enterprises that are small is higher than the proportion of manufacturers because

  1 services offer fewer opportunities for technical economies of scale
  2 services are usually more labour intensive than manufacturers
  3 markets for services tend to be more localised than markets for manufactured goods

7
The firm and the market

Topic summary

Importance and nature of marketing

Marketing is the term given to those activities directed towards ensuring that the enterprise produces and distributes products that people are able to buy at prices and in quantities capable of enabling the firm to achieve its business objectives.

In the private sector profit objectives must inevitably be extremely important. In the public sector, where profit may not be relevant, marketing may still take place to ensure that organisations are meeting the wishes of the electorate as expressed through the political machinery of the community.

Marketing and selling

The term marketing is sometimes used as though it were just another word for selling. It is far more than this. Selling is the activity of persuading and assisting people to buy products that the organisation is actually producing. The organisation has committed itself to certain forms of production and sales departments have to play their part in helping the organisation to achieve its objectives by doing everything possible to persuade people to buy. Marketing, however, is a much wider activity which involves forecasting future market trends, relating these to the organisation's resources and advising management on future production in the light of predicted future developments. It clearly involves co-operation with production managers over product development, pricing and design. It also involves the choice and cultivation of distribution channels.

Selling is a matter of tactics to achieve the successful conclusion of plans already adopted.

Marketing is concerned with the strategic formulation of plans designed to achieve organisational objectives.

Both are necessary for the long term success of the organisation. In the short term skilful selling can sometimes conceal inadequate marketing. In the long term no amount of inspired selling can save the organisation from the consequences of failing to carry out adequate marketing.

The marketing mix

Elements of the marketing mix include the following:

Market research

This requires investigation of future market trends and is likely to include the examination of trends in population growth and age structure, changes in income levels, in the geographical location of buyers, in government policies as they affect incomes, location and other factors influencing buying decisions. It will take into account trends in public attitudes (e.g. over environmental issues) and the general matter of taste. Such research may now need to include many nations and regions of the world.

Product demand forecasting

As well as examining the general shape and direction of market trends research must be directed towards estimating probable demand for specific products at given ranges of prices. This involves identifying the main influences on product demand, the relative strengths of those influences and their likely future trends.

In formal terms this can most effectively be achieved by setting up a model which can be used for prediction and for answering those 'what if' questions that assist in the choice of price, advertising and promotion expenditure, etc.

For example, we can expect that the demand for most products is likely to be influenced by their own prices (P_o), other prices (P_a), buyers' disposable incomes (Y_d), i.e. incomes after deduction of taxes and other compulsory payments, the availability of money and credit (M), advertising expenditure (A), market size, i.e. number of potential buyers (N), and any special factors (v) relating to the product, such as, weather in the case of drinks.

The symbols in brackets enable us to express the above statement as a demand function in the form:

$$Qd = f(P_o, P_a, Y_d, M, A, N, v)$$

This is still a general statement and to become a working model the general symbol 'f', meaning 'is a function of' needs to be replaced by a series of coefficients indicating the relative strengths of each separate influence. The model thus takes the general form:

$$Qd_x = aP_o + bP_a + cY_d + dM + eA + gN + hv$$

Researchers have to estimate the values of the coefficients relevant to the products and keep these values under review; estimate future trends in those, such as income and other prices, which are outside the organisation's control and estimate the consequences of changes in those, such as price and advertising expenditure, which are within their control. Complete accuracy, of course, is virtually impossible to achieve and research is a continuous process.

Price

Any influence on product demand which can be altered by the organisation must be part of the marketing mix. The pricing decision is, of course, of crucial importance. The market itself will have some expectation about the price range for the product and the price chosen, when compared with the prices of close rivals, will signal the firm's estimation of relative quality of the product and the general pattern of its marketing approach. Pricing issues are examined more fully in a later unit.

Advertising and product promotion

No product sells itself. There always has to be some effort to bring it to the attention of potential buyers and to distinguish it from rival products. Enormous efforts are often made to establish and maintain instantly recognisable brand images and names. At the most successful level the brand name becomes the label for an entire class of product; examples include 'biro' and 'hoover'. Linked with advertising are packaging, point of sale displays and promotions and a range of other ways of bringing the product to the attention of potential buyers.

It is the responsibility of the marketing department to manage campaigns and promotions and choose the media as well as the general approach.

The effectiveness of advertising is one of those questions which is almost incapable of receiving a direct, simple answer. We may accept the general statement that the more we spend on advertising the greater the quantity we are likely to sell but how much more depends on further matters such as the quality of the advertising message and approach and the quality and amount of spending by rivals. We must also recognise that the advertising budget is almost invariably the first to be cut whenever the firm believes it is entering a period of general market recession. We may be tempted to regard this as a vote of no confidence by senior management in the effectiveness of advertising but it can also be seen as a common sense approach to the reality of the market changes taking place in a recession. However much an individual may want to buy a new family car, attractive advertising will not overcome the fact that a falling family income or fear of redundancy will be much more powerful forces telling the person that there can be no new car this year. Clearly it is better to delay the advertising until rising incomes and brighter future prospects are persuading people that a new car has now become possible. During the period of recession when incomes are under threat a more powerful influence is likely to be a significant price reduction or a move to make credit more easily available. This, of course, suggests that the firm has to produce not just a single demand model but a number of different models for particular market conditions.

At the same time it also seems probable that advertising is seen by many firms as a form of residual expenditure which can be varied in order to maintain profit stability. Advertising budgets can be raised when profits are rising and cut when they are falling.

Advertising and promotional expenditure is frequently classified as **above the line** and **below the line**. Above the line spending is aimed at increasing sales in specific markets with specific and known target audiences. In contrast below the line spending is less direct and aimed at raising the profile of the firm or product in the public consciousness. Most spending on major sport sponsorship is below the line and it can often an effective way of bringing to general attention a previously little known name.

Distribution channels

The firm has to ensure that the product is available for purchase at the place where the people most likely to buy expect to find it. However much we may prefer brand X few of us are going to go to great lengths to search for it when the roughly equivalent brand Y is just around the corner waiting to be bought. Now that an increasing proportion of total consumer purchases are made through a relatively few large stores the choice of distribution channel may be limited and much effort is made to ensure that the product is given a favourable location within the store. Store managers, of course, also want to ensure that the best selling points are reserved for the products achieving the highest levels of profit so that location, shelf space, etc become involved with other elements of the marketing mix, especially advertising, price, distributor margins and packaging.

Marketing consistency

All the elements of the marketing mix must make a consistent pattern. Price, advertising and distribution channel must all send the same signals about quality and must all be aimed at the same target audience of potential buyers. A frequent approach to new product promotion is to adopt a luxury, up-market image with above average price and a general impression of quality, aiming at the more affluent sections of the community who are usually believed to be the pioneers in trying new products. This strategy reduces the risks of initial production because full production need not be embarked upon until the product's success is assured. If the product is successful its price can be reduced relative to rival prices and the sales approach changed to appeal to the larger market.

Techniques of market analysis

Much of the information needed for market research and demand estimation is already available somewhere. At the same time some, specific to the product or to current market conditions may have to be discovered by investigation. Sources of information are thus either secondary (already existing) or primary (requiring investigation).

Secondary sources are unlikely to be in the form required by the marketing department so tapping them involves skills of location, selection and presentation. Much information is available in public reference libraries and in the statistical tables prepared by central and local government agencies but it has to be extracted, interpreted and presented in a form intelligible to people who are not specialist statisticians. Most firms, other than very large firms, are likely to make use of specialist market research organisations. These also tend to have banks of data useful to many companies so they offer the general benefits of specialisation in that they avoid duplication of effort as well as developing special skills and knowledge.

Primary sources have to be investigated, usually through the use of a sample or samples. Ideally, the sample should contain all the different characteristics of the full target audience but be small enough to be subjected to careful and controlled investigation. This again involves statistical techniques which are familiar to the main market research organisations.

Investigation may take the form of survey and questionnaires, also requiring specialised skills, or 'laboratory tests', as, for example, when a chosen sample is given a sum of money to spend on a range of goods and investigators seek to identify the main influences on their choices.

As a final test before actual launch a new product is sometimes put into small scale production and then **test marketed** in selected areas and stores. The sales path is then charted and if this conforms to a predicted pattern the product is launched, possibly after modifications seen to be desirable in the light of the test. This is claimed to be a reliable indicator of future success but it is expensive and many costs will have been sunk before the test market stage can be reached. Another problem is that competitors are forewarned and given the chance to bring forward a rival promotion.

All investigations and predictions should carry the warning that the future can never be forecast with complete certainty. Most techniques for predicting future market trends and product sales patterns involve the projection of past tendencies into the future in some way. If something happens in the future which has not happened in the period investigated, the prediction is likely to wrong. Of course, allowance should always be made for eventualities likely to take place in the future but these are difficult to foresee if they have not occurred in the past. The one certain fact about the future is its uncertainty. Consequently, any business decision taken about the future must always remain something of a gamble. Business decision-making can never be purely mathematical. There is always room for personal judgement (and misjudgment) about what will happen tomorrow. This is why business produces more bankruptcies than millionaires. The value of systematic and skilled research is that it takes account of the predictable and allows the business manager to focus attention on the unpredictable where there is no escape from the need to form a judgement. This is the danger — and the fascination — of business management.

The product life cycle

This is probably one of the best known concepts of marketing. It indicates the path that all products that become established eventually have to take. ·It is best illustrated by the familiar diagram (Figure 7.1) showing the various stages of the cycle.

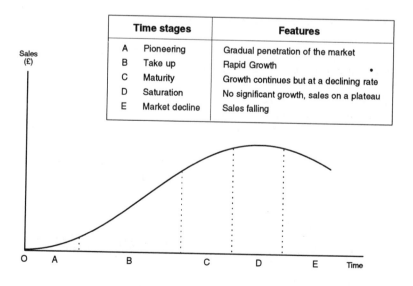

Time stages		Features
A	Pioneering	Gradual penetration of the market
B	Take up	Rapid Growth
C	Maturity	Growth continues but at a declining rate
D	Saturation	No significant growth, sales on a plateau
E	Market decline	Sales falling

Figure 7.1 The product life cycle

There is little dispute about the characteristics of the stages represented in this cycle, from pioneering through growth, maturity, saturation to decline, but there is no way of predicting the length of each stage of the cycle. Some products, e.g. the well known table sauces and a number of breakfast cereals, have a very long sales plateau spreading over several generations of consumers. Others, such as many types of clothing and children's toys, have a very short cycle measured in months rather than years but may re-appear from time to time.

Nor is it easy to predict the turning point of each cycle. Recognising a terminal downturn can be extremely difficult when previous sales dips have been successfully checked with small product modifications or marketing campaigns. Sometimes the final drop can come suddenly after a long period on the plateau.

The concept of the product life cycle stands as a warning to every marketing manager, indicating the need to be ready for eventual decline and to have new products available as the old fade away. As an aid to future demand forecasting, however, it is of little use.

Discussion and revision questions

- 'A really effective marketing department should not have to rely on a force of super salespeople.' Why not?

- If an institution of higher education were to appoint a marketing manager what would be this manager's functions?

- Why is it important for marketing managers to take note of projected movements in future income levels?

- What would you expect to be the main influences on the demand for the following: individually owned, new, private cars; package holidays in the Mediterranean; national daily newspapers.

- Discuss the view that large scale advertising of consumer products is a wasteful activity and that both producers and consumers would obtain greater benefits from reducing prices.

- 'Surely the simplest way to conduct a sample survey is to go out into the street and question the first hundred people you meet.' Explain why this would **not** provide a satisfactory sample survey.

- Why are postal surveys almost always unreliable?

- The product life cycle has been called one of the best known and least useful concepts in marketing. Suggest reasons for this description.

- Suggest reasons why the main breakfast cereal manufacturers have produced a range of different branded cereals instead of concentrating their resources on just one or two.

Suggestions for individual or team projects

- Watch the advertising on a commercial television network over several evenings at peak viewing times. Note the products and the product brands advertised. With help from your reference library and by studying any details of manufacturers shown on product packaging try to establish the identity of the advertising companies. Comment on the similarities and differences in the market structure (number and size of producers, nature of market competition) of the heavily advertised products.

- Choose two different products (e.g. one consumer durable and one non-durable). Examine any similarities and differences you can detect in:

  (a) pricing policies, e.g. is there price competition among different suppliers?

  (b) extent of advertising and choice of advertising media (e.g. t.v., press).

  (c) distribution channels including types of store where most sales are made.

  Discuss and suggest explanations for your findings.

8
Pricing in practice

Topic summary

Economic theory and pricing

Economists commonly point out that there are two contrasting market environments within which business managers may be called upon to take their pricing decisions. They are likely to be operating in one or other of the following:

- Markets where the individual firm has little or no discretion to set its own product prices because these are established either by the interaction of total market supply and demand which the individual firm on its own cannot alter or by a regulatory body acting under the authority of the State.
- Markets where the individual firm is a sufficiently powerful supplier to be able to influence market price or to set its own product prices.

Where the firm is in the first market environment it has to accept the market price as a **price taker**. Under these conditions it may also have little power over the prices of its main factor and resource inputs and all its managerial skills must be devoted to choosing the most profitable level at which to produce. This will be particularly important if its products cannot be stored for any significant length of time. In these conditions over production becomes a very dangerous hazard. Managers must be alert for possible shifts in the market or regulated price because a price change shifts the most desirable production level and in modern factor markets it is not always easy to make swift changes in quantities purchased. Workers cannot be summarily dismissed and any significant reduction in the size of the workforce can lead to expensive redundancy and other 'severance' costs. Consequently, success or failure for the firm frequently involves difficult purchasing and production decisions.

Where the firm is in a position to be able to set its own selling prices it still has to take into account many factors including:

- Its own input and production costs.

- Demand conditions in the markets within which the firm is seeking to operate.
- The pricing decisions and other elements of the marketing strategies of rival firms in the market. The more concentrated and oligopolistic the market, i.e. the fewer and larger the rival suppliers the more important this becomes. A high proportion of consumer products are now sold in large, self- or semi-self-service stores where competing brands are displayed side-by-side providing potential buyers with ample scope to make price comparisons.
- Opportunities for distinguishing the product from its rivals in order to give more flexibility in pricing and to reduce the importance of price as an influencing factor in demand. For example, firms may use advertising, including point-of-sale advertising, brand image, and packaging to foster a consumer perception of quality, thus justifying a premium price compared with rival brands. Non-standard weights and unusual designs for packages are other devices intended to discourage price comparisons and foster a perception that the product has no close substitutes.

Pricing and business objectives

The point has been made in an earlier unit that assuming the firm is seeking simply to maximise its profits is not an adequate basis for understanding its behaviour. Even if we follow a number of modern economists in regarding the maximisation of the firm's value as the most likely long-term business objective this still leaves open a range of short-term objectives. They may all be reconcilable to long-term value maximisation but can still be in conflict with each other in the short term. If a firm pursues revenue, as opposed to profit maximisation, in the short run it will adopt a different pricing strategy. This will be different again for a policy, say, of maximising market share in the hope of securing greater future freedom in setting price and other marketing elements. A brief outline of some of the possible alternatives to profit maximisation was given in Unit 5. Figure 8.1 gives a further illustration of the implications of abandoning the profit-maximising assumption for the pricing strategy of the firm.

This shows that the firm which has a significant amount of power in the market is able to operate at a profit over a substantial range of output, in this model between output levels Oq_o and Oq_2, i.e. between the two break-even points where average revenue just equals average cost. Consequently it is not essential for the firm to maximise profits but can make what its own senior managers and its financial advisers may regard as satisfactory profits and pursue other objectives at the expense of some profit. If other objectives such as revenue and expansion are pursued consumers are likely to receive benefits in the form of increased market supply and lower prices compared with the profit-maximising position.

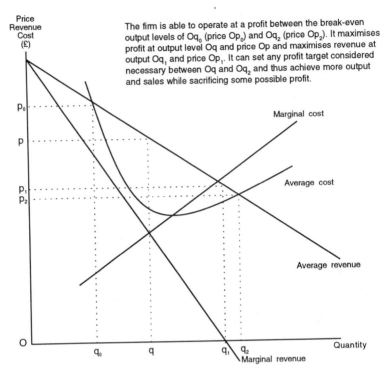

The firm is able to operate at a profit between the break-even output levels of Oq_0 (price Op_0) and Oq_2 (price Op_2). It maximises profit at output level Oq and price Op and maximises revenue at output Oq_1 and price Op_1. It can set any profit target considered necessary between Oq and Oq_2 and thus achieve more output and sales while sacrificing some possible profit.

Figure 8.1 Some pricing strategies for the firm possessing market power

For the firm, the possession of market power affords the opportunity to set prices and pursue objectives without being forced to profit maximise.

Formula pricing

No firm which is not a 'natural monopoly' providing an essential service such as water or electricity supply can set prices with complete freedom. Demand conditions ensure that there will always be a relationship between the price charged for the product and the quantity people are prepared to buy. Market expectations set constraints on managerial freedom to set price. At the same time firms can only survive if they make profits and they can only operate successfully within the price and output zone where total revenue is greater than total cost (between Oq_0 and Oq_2 in Figure 8.1). We might say then that the art of successful pricing lies very much in the ability to reconcile the often conflicting pressures of buyer demand and supplier costs.

What tends to happen in many cases is that the firm establishes a price level and estimates a quantity level which its appraisal of the market suggests can be sold at that price and then develops a **formula** calculated to arrive at the desired price. This is likely to involve a calculation of the total costs and their division by quantity employed of a major, essential input such as labour. The result may be to produce a formula for setting price by reference to an amount per hour of labour likely to be used for a particular production process. The more labour a product or activity uses the more it will use other inputs so that the formula should ensure that production remains profitable. It also provides a mechanism to change price in response to a significant change in the prices of one or more of the other inputs. The hourly labour charge resulting from the formula should not be taken as being the hourly wage rate paid to workers.

Full cost pricing

Most formula pricing systems are variations of what is often called **full-cost pricing** in that all inputs are listed and their costs included and used to produce an average or unit cost. This unit cost is increased by a percentage mark-up as desired by the firm's management and the result is the unit price. The logic of any kind of full-cost pricing system is that input costs are not overlooked and, if the formula has been calculated accurately the firm should be able to make a profit.

On the other hand the stress placed on costs can lead to a neglect of buyer expectations. As costs rise there is the temptation to increase prices until they move into that area where demand falls rapidly in response to price rises. Even before that any rise in price above the profit-maximising level (Oq in Figure 8.1) will reduce profits.

In any full cost formula it is important to distinguish between variable and fixed costs. In most cases the variable cost per unit of product can be calculated without too much difficulty. A piece of furniture will require a certain input of wood or other material; a garment requires a certain amount of cloth. These amounts, plus an allowance for waste can be apportioned to the cost of each unit. It is also possible to apportion machine and process labour time in much the same way.

It is, however, more difficult to apportion other fixed costs where there is no clear and definite relationship with production volume. These have to be taken into account in the costing. It is simple enough to calculate an average fixed cost provided the production quantity is known. An assumption also has to be made about quantity in order to calculate machine cost. Depreciation, maintenance and repair costs have to be apportioned assuming a particular level of production. Nevertheless it is unrealistic to try and estimate the quantity that is likely to be sold — and it is little use producing goods unless these can be sold — without knowing the probable price. Here then is the problem. Price, or a range of possible prices must be assumed in order to estimate sales quantity. Probable quantities to be sold and produced must be assumed in order to calculate cost on which price is to be based.

In practice, production and marketing departments have to co-operate to work out estimates for both price and quantity given a range of possible price-output combinations. If it becomes clear that a product cannot be produced at a cost and hence a price that seems likely to generate the volume of sales required then it will not be produced. In the case of new products the need to achieve a given combination of price and quantity will determine target sales figures that must be achieved within given periods for production to be continued. The firm will have its own targets for the profit returns it expects from each of its products and those which cannot meet the targets will be abandoned unless there are compelling reasons for deciding otherwise.

Certain costs, such as general administration, or 'Head Office' expenses, which cannot be directly linked with specific products or activities are often allocated in a rather arbitrary fashion. Very often the established products are required to carry a high proportion of these costs while newer products, in spite of providing much of the work carried out by the commercial and service departments tend to carry a relatively smaller burden. There is thus a degree of cross subsidisation from the established products requiring little support from the service departments to the newer products which depend heavily on support.

Over reliance on a rigid cost-based formula can lead to failure to undertake profitable work. If the firm has spare resources the opportunity cost of these can be very low. Any opportunity to put these to profitable use can contribute to profits provided:

- the payment received is greater than the additional variable costs incurred.
- no offence is given to other customers paying prices based on full average cost.

On the other hand failure to appreciate the true additional costs of extra output can lead to heavy losses. If resources are already fully employed on current production and additional work is offered requiring substantial extra fixed costs, e.g. if another machine has to be bought, this extra cost can only be justified if the increase in output is likely to be sustained and improved. Otherwise the extra fixed cost will simply raise average fixed costs for existing output and reduce existing profit margins.

It is essential to remember that final average costs can only be calculated when the **sales** figures are known. If goods remain unsold then earlier estimates of average costs have to be revised. Pricing to a formula can never guarantee a profit. The profit anticipated by the formula can only materialise if the sales assumptions on which the formula was based turn out to be correct.

Price and the marketing mix

It is a fundamental assumption in economics and in business practice that there is always a relationship between price and the quantity that can be sold. It is generally assumed that a reduction in price will increase quantity sold. However, the strength of this relationship can vary enormously and in all cases price is only **one** of a range of factors influencing buyers' decisions.

This idea is given more formal expression through the measures known as demand elasticities. These were explained in Unit 2. If demand for a product is price inelastic a price reduction will **reduce** revenue. The quantity sold will increase but this will not be sufficient to compensate for the revenue lost from the price reduction over the former quantity level. In this case revenues can be increased by a price rise but the consequent fall in sales volume will reduce market share and may lead to a further deterioration in demand in the longer term.

If profits are not considered to be sufficient on a product whose demand is price inelastic it may be desirable to combine a price rise with additional spending on advertising or product promotion or by some modification of the product or its packaging to try and make it more appealing to buyers.

In practice it is not always easy to estimate price elasticities of demand especially where other factors are significant. Prices cannot be changed too frequently. Price alterations involve expense for producers and distributors. Most markets have conventions governing the frequency and timing of price changes and suppliers flout these at their peril. A firm may suspect that it could raise price with little effect on demand but having made the change it must live with it for a time even if sales do fall more than expected. Moreover, the price change will have altered the market's perception of the product and there is no guarantee that a price reduction will restore the former position.

It is essential to distinguish between the demand elasticities for the class of product and any one brand. If all suppliers of canned dog food raise prices by a few pence per can, total sales might not be much changed but if prices are raised for one or two brands only, there may well be a significant shift in buyer support to brands whose prices stay unchanged. The greater the degree of perceived substitutability between competing brands, i.e. the more willing people are to switch brands, the more price elastic the brands are likely to be. To overcome this suppliers will seek to confuse prices by adopting a range of different package sizes so that one package may appear cheaper than another while actually being dearer on a price per gramme basis. They will also seek to convince buyers that their brands have unique features to discourage price comparisons. The aim is clearly to ensure that the brand is no more, and preferably less, price elastic than the class of product itself.

Price discrimination

This occurs when the supplier charges different prices to different customers for what is broadly the same product purchased in the same broad time period. Discretion to charge different prices must remain with the supplier. A discount offered, say, for bulk purchase to any buyer meeting certain stated conditions is not price discrimination as the choice is with the buyer.

Four types of price discrimination are commonly identified. These are:

- **Perfect discrimination**
  This is achieved by haggling with each buyer in an attempt to charge the price equal to that buyer's marginal utility. If successful this eliminates consumer surplus and produces the largest possible amount of sales revenue. It is illustrated in Figure 8.2.

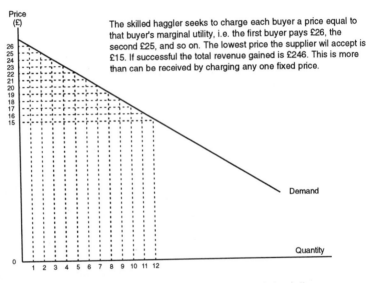

Figure 8.2 Perfect price discrimination through haggling

Attempting such total discrimination is only practicable where the haggler has a financial interest in the outcome, e.g. as business owner or salesperson receiving commission, where the number of individual transactions is small relative to the time available for selling and where the activities of any employed person trusted to negotiate prices can be monitored. It is only profitable if the costs are less than the additional revenue obtained.

- **Favoured buyers**
  Favouring particular buyers with price terms not available to others. It is assumed that the amount of price reduction allowed is greater than could be justified by cost savings achieved through such means as bulk

purchase. Such discrimination is usually the result of the market power of the buyer or buyers. Provided the net additional revenue is greater than the net additional costs of supply this will increase profits. However, if the sales to the favoured customer or customers represent a high proportion of the supplier's total sales turnover so that losing the customer's business would seriously damage the firm, the supplier is vulnerable to any further pressure to reduce prices. The effect of supplying a favoured customer is illustrated in Figure 8.3.

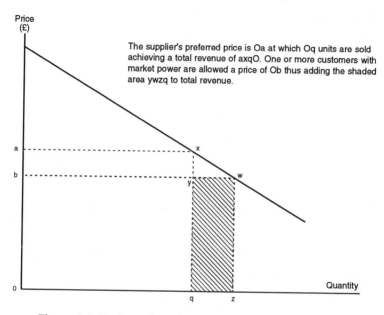

Figure 8.3 Perfect price discrimination through haggling

- **Market sectors**
  Supplying different sectors of a market when the sectors can be segregated and have different price elasticities of demand. If one sector of a market is less sensitive to price rises than the other then there is a clear possibility that total revenue could be increased if prices in that sector were raised and prices in the other sector reduced. It also seems likely that shifting part of the quantity sold from the less to the more price-sensitive market will produce a gain in revenue. If we assume that the firm is seeking to maximise profits we can produce a model to show that this will indeed be the result. The model is illustrated in Figure 8.4.

Here the revenue gain is clear. Provided the increase in revenue is greater than any increase in costs resulting from treating the market as two distinct markets then there will also be a profits gain. This principle is used by public transport undertakings such as British Rail and the airlines in their fare structures. Markets are usually distinguished by the time of travel. The lower fares are charged at times which are normally impractical for most business travellers who are less sensitive to price changes than private individuals travelling for leisure and paying their own fares.

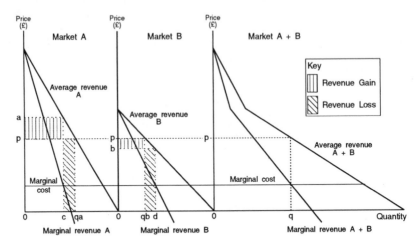

Figure 8.4 Segregating markets which have different price elasticities of demand

Market A is less price sensitive than market B. If there is no segregation the profit-maximising price in the combined market (A + B) is Op with quantity sold (Oq) shared on the basis of Oqa (market A) and Oqb (market B). If there is price discrimination the profit-maximising prices are Oa (market A) and Ob (market B). Some sales (qa – c) are lost in market A but an equivalent quantity of sales is gained (d – qd) in market B. However, the revenue gain is greater than the revenue loss and as there is no change in costs profit is increased as a result of price discrimination.

- **Pricing to use spare capacity**
  If the firm has spare production capacity in the form, say, of unused machine time then any order gained at a unit price higher than the average variable costs such as materials and labour, will add to profits. This is because the additional revenue gained over and above the variable costs contribute to those fixed costs which have to be paid whether the order is gained or not. Such a price is likely to be lower than the firm's normal price which will have been calculated on the basis of securing a margin of profit above the average **total** (variable + fixed) costs. This, of course, will only be successful if care is taken not to upset existing customers paying the higher prices!

Transfer pricing

A transfer price refers to the price charged when goods or services are sold from one part of an organisation to another part of the same organisation. Transfer prices are usually part of a general attempt to assess separately the efficiency and profitability of different parts of the large organisation.

Transfer prices help to determine the relative profitability of the various sectors of the organisation and they can also serve to compare the performance of the internal sector with outside suppliers.

The general rule for setting transfer prices, assuming a desire to profit maximise, is to set transfer price equal to market price if there is a market in the transferred good or service. Unless there is a compelling reason the firm will not wish to produce at a cost higher than the price that can be paid in the external market. On the other hand if the firm is able to produce more than it can itself use at the market price it can enter the market as a supplier.

If there is no market price, i.e. no external suppliers of the transferred good or service, then the profit-maximising rule would normally be to set the transfer price at the marginal cost of production at the desired quantity level.

In practice these rules are frequently broken for such considerations as the desire to retain complete control over part of the production process, the desire to minimise liability to taxes on business profits or to by-pass national laws on the export of profits. National governments will seek to prevent the use of transfer pricing to evade their laws but without a detailed knowledge of the production processes involved, detection of evasion is often difficult.

Pricing for other specific objectives

It has already been pointed out that price is one element in the total marketing mix and pricing is an instrument which can be used both strategically and tactically. The large, multi-product firm may be prepared to operate at a loss, in the short term, over part of its production range in order, say, to enter a market or to encourage buyers to buy other products with higher profit margins. The loss leader approach has long been familiar in retailing where one product is advertised at a very low price to encourage people to enter the store. Attractive displays may then encourage enough impulse buying of profitable lines to increase total profit.

Prices can also be used to discourage entry of competitors or, if new competitors do appear, the established firms may be willing to suffer a loss for a period long enough to drive out the newcomers. These tactics are more likely to be successful if potential new entrants are smaller firms with higher production costs than the established suppliers. Pricing is not a defence against a powerful competitor, such as a foreign company, already well established in related or similar foreign markets.

Discussion and revision questions

- Explain, with the help of a diagram, why the major decisions of a firm operating in a market approximating to perfect competition are likely to relate to production rather than price decisions.

- It is often said that however powerful a firm it can only choose **either** price **or** output level but never both. Explain the basis for this statement with the help of a diagram.

- Explain and illustrate the statement that for a firm in a perfectly competitive market profit maximisation is a survival condition, but for a firm with significant market power it is not.

- What would you expect to be the most common form of formula pricing used by service organisations? What are the advantages and dangers of this method of pricing?

- 'Future output can only be planned if future sales figures can be estimated. These cannot be estimated unless a price has been decided and price is based on costs which can only be calculated if an output figure is known.' What kind of pricing system is being assumed in this statement? Explain how the dilemma expressed in the statement arises. Suggest possible ways it may be overcome.

- 'Price cannot be determined in isolation from the other elements in the marketing mix.' What are these other elements? What is their relevance to price?

- Choose one of the following products: bread; canned pet food; canned fruit or vegetables; breakfast cereal. Visit one or two large superstores and study the various brands of your chosen product. Discuss the following features: ranges of prices; ranges of packet or can weights; any other features used to distinguish between brands; number of firms supplying the product; number and features of brands offered by each supplier.

- Why do some airlines offer reduced fares for passengers willing to make a firm, unalterable booking several weeks before travel and provided they stay at their destination over a weekend?

- A firm produces blodgetts under the following cost conditions:

Office and administration expenses	£2500 per month
Marketing costs	£3000 per month
Materials used in manufacture	£5 per unit
Machine capable of making 100 blodgetts per day:	
depreciation & leasing costs	£1000 per month
wages of machinist	£50 per day

Over the past year sales have averaged around 1500 per month. The firm seeks to achieve a profit before tax of £2 per blodgett. There are 20 normal working days in each month. What price should it charge to achieve this at the current sales level? What price would you expect the firm to charge if current sales (a) dropped by 20% or (b) increased by 20%?

A potential new customer offers to pay £3200 for 400 blodgetts to be collected in one month's time. Should the firm accept this offer? Justify your answer.

- Firms launching a new product sometimes set the price above that ruling for roughly comparable products produced by rival suppliers. Suggest reasons for this.

- In the 1960s sugar was a product frequently used by supermarkets as a loss leader. The standard 2lb bags of granulated sugar were stacked at the end of the store furthest from the entrance. What did the supermarket hope to achieve by this practice? Why is sugar no longer used in this way? Suggest reasons why loss leaders are used less frequently than in the past by modern superstores?

Multiple choice questions

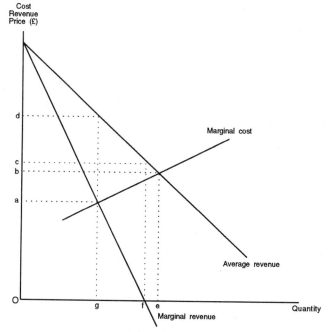

Figure 8.5

- The firm whose cost and revenue position is represented by Figure 8.5 would maximise its profits if it charged a price of

  A Oa
  B Ob
  C Oc
  D Od

- The firm whose cost and revenue position is represented by Figure 8.5 would maximise its revenue if it charged a price of

  A Oa
  B Ob
  C Oc
  D Od

- In the long run as compared with the short run the firm can expect that its product's market

  A demand is more price elastic and supply less elastic
  B demand is less price elastic and supply more elastic
  C demand and supply are less price elastic
  D demand and supply are more price elastic

- If a firm changed from maximising profit to maximising revenue we would expect its product

  A prices to rise and output fall
  B prices to fall and output rise
  C prices and output to fall
  D prices and output to rise

- Organisations which are natural monopolies have a large amount of freedom to choose the price and output levels that are in their own interests. Assuming that this freedom can be controlled in the public interest by regulatory bodies we would expect such a body to operate in the market for

  A potatoes
  B gas
  C petrol
  D timber

- A service organisation sets its prices by adding to the cost of any goods supplied a labour charge of £20 an hour. The average wage paid to labour in this firm is £12. This difference indicates that the firm is

  A making monopoly profits
  B adopting a formula pricing system
  C charging what the market will bear
  D adopting price discrimination

- A firm's marketing manager estimates that, for a proposed new product, yearly sales of 50 000 units can be achieved at a unit price of £80 and 60 000 units at a price of £70. The production manager estimates that average variable costs of production would be £30 and fixed production costs, £1 000 000 per year. Average marketing and distribution costs are known to be £10 and fixed administration, marketing and distribution costs, £500 000. The directors have established a profit target for all new products of 10% of sales turnover (minimum £400 000) by the end of the first year. On the basis of these figures

  A the firm could produce either 50 000 or 60 000 units of the product
  B the product should not be produced at either of the proposed quantity levels
  C the firm should produce 50 000 units and set price at £80
  D the firm should produce 60 000 units and set price at £80

- Further marketing research by the firm in the previous question indicates that 40 000 units could be sold in a year at a unit price of £90 and 30 000 units at a price of £100. On this basis the firm could

  A increase profits by charging £90 instead of £80 or £70
  B continue to increase profits by charging £100
  C maintain profits but reduce revenue by charging £90 instead of £80 or £70
  D maximise revenue and profit at a price of £80

- Large-scale brand advertising is designed to

  A increase the brand's price elasticity of demand
  B reduce the brand's price elasticity of demand
  C increase the brand's substitutability for other brands
  D reduce the brand's price elasticity of supply

- Price discrimination will not benefit the supplier if

  A groups of buyers have different price elasticities of demand
  B communications within the market are poor
  C buyers have different perceptions of marginal utility
  D charging different prices adds more to costs than to revenue

9

Business investment

Topic summary

The investment decision

In business the investment decision concerns deciding whether or not to spend a sum of money (devote some available scarce resources) to a particular project now in the belief that this will help towards the achievement of the organisation's objectives in the future.

The objective normally assumed for a business firm in the private sector is that of maximising profit but the financial appraisal techniques explained in this unit can be applied to other objectives as long as they can be given monetary values. For non-financial objectives, e.g. to achieve a target reduction in the rate of infant child mortality, different techniques are necessary but the basic nature of the investment decision remains the same. This is to try and estimate whether the proposed expenditure of resources will make a sufficient contribution to the achievement of objectives for it to be considered worthwhile by those responsible for those resources. In this unit we confine our attention to financial investment designed to increase the profits of the investing organisation.

A crucial element of investment is the difference in time between the expenditure of resources and the receipt of returns from the investment project. Expenditure is usually to be made **now** or in the near future. The returns are usually to be expected in the more distant future. Since a comparison is to be made between the present spending and the receipts expected in the future, care is needed to:

- obtain as much reliable information about the project as possible, about its anticipated lifetime and the amount of financial return that can be expected during that lifetime and about the uncertainties that surround these predictions of the future.
- compare like with like bearing in mind that £1 paid today is not the same as £1 received tomorrow not only because the purchasing power may be

eroded by general price rises but also because money has an earning power and can earn interest, the loss of which has to be taken into account when considering whether or not to spend now.

In practice, business firms frequently find themselves having to decide between competing projects. If project A is chosen then project B will have to be abandoned because there are not sufficient resources for both or because the risk of borrowing sufficient money to undertake all available projects is considered too heavy.

All investment projects have to be considered against the background of the strategic development of the organisation. Project A may offer more immediate profits than project B but if project B is believed to make a greater contribution towards taking the organisation along the road it has decided to follow to achieve its long term goals then project B is more likely to be favoured.

Investment appraisal techniques

Because investment appraisal usually involves the allocation of finance it is also commonly referred to as **capital budgeting**.

Payback period

Simple payback is the simplest and most widely understood of all appraisal methods. The payback period is the period needed for the cost of the project to be returned through the increased net income which it produces. Thus, projects costing £100 000 which generated an increase in profits of £20 000 a year would have a payback period of 5 years. This is called simple payback because no attempt is made to allow for the time difference between future profit receipts and the immediate cost of the project.

Discounting

The method used to eliminate the value differences resulting from time is called **discounting.** This simply means modifying a future payment by whatever discount rate or discount factor is considered to provide adequate compensation, over the relevant time period, for the loss of the money's earning power, any anticipated decline in purchasing power caused by general price inflation and for uncertainty which can upset the most carefully researched and prepared plans.

Choice of a suitable discount rate requires financial skill and the ability to form judgements about probable future trends. The starting point is the interest rate which the money needed for the project would earn if invested in the finance market. This rate is modified according to anticipations of future interest rate trends and the considerations of inflation and uncertainty already mentioned.

Present values

The formula used to calculate the **present value** (V_o) of a single payment due to be paid at the end of n years (V_n) can be expressed in the form

$$V_o = V_n \div (1+d)^n$$

where d = the rate of discount expressed as a decimal fraction (e.g. 10% as 0.1, 8% as 0.08)

For example the present value of £1000 due to be paid at the end of 3 years discounted at 15% is £1000 ÷ (1.15)³ which is £1000 ÷ 1.5209 = £657.51.

To check this value and to see more clearly what discounting really implies assume that the present sum of £657.51 is deposited in an account paying interest at 15% payable at the end of each year.

At the end of year 1 interest of £98.63 (15% of £657.51) is added to £657.51 making a total of £756.14
At the end of year 2 interest of £113.42 (15% of £756.14) is added to £756.14 making a total of £869.56
At the end of year 3 interest of £130.44 (15% of £869.56) is added to £869.56 making a total of £1000

An investment project, however, will produce, not a single future payment, but a flow of payments spread over a given period in the future and the present value of such a flow is found from the formula

$$V_o = V_1 \div (1 + d) + V_2 \div (1 + d)^2 + V_3 \div (1 + d)^3 + \dots + V_n \div (1 + d)^n$$

It is clear that discounting has an increasing effect as the time lengthens. This can be shown using the earlier simple payback example. The project costing £100 000 earned £20 000 per year. Assuming that the £20 000 is received at the end of each year and adopting a discount rate, constant in each year, of 10%, a short table of present values for each of the future payments can be produced.

Present value	Future payment at the end of	n year(s)
£18 181.82	£20 000	1
£16 528.93	£20 000	2
£15 026.30	£20 000	3
£13 660.27	£20 000	4
£12 418.43	£20 000	5
£11 289.48	£20 000	6
£10 263.16	£20 000	7
£ 9 330.15	£20 000	8

When there was no discounting the payback period was 5 years but now that future payments have been discounted at a rate of 10% only the present value of £75 815.75 is paid by the end of the fifth year and it is not until the end of the 8th year that the cost of the project is recovered. Notice that in this 8th year the present value is less than half the future payment.

Net present value

The **net present value** of a project is the present value of the stream of future profits attributable to the project over its lifetime, **less the cost of the project**. In the above example the total of all the present values for each of the 8 years is £106 698.54. Suppose the projected life of the project is just 8 years then the total present value of the 8 payments of £20 000, discounted at 10% is £106 698.54. Subtracting the project's cost of £100 000 leaves a **net present value** of £6 698.54. If the figures are judged to be realistic, if a constant 10% discount rate over the 8 year period is the result of a realistic assessment of all the considerations involved and if the firm is willing to wait 8 years to recover its initial outlay then we can say that the project does add to profits and may be proceeded with unless the firm can find a more profitable investment project. If the firm has to choose, say, one from several competing investment projects then, if there were no powerful reasons to do otherwise, it would adopt the one with the largest net present value provided that the payback period did not exceed the length of time considered to be the minimum by the firm's decision makers.

Internal rate of return

A similar process of discounting is used to produce **the internal rate of return** (IRR). This is the rate of discount which produces a net present value of zero, i.e. which brings the present value to equality with the project's cost. Consider the following example. For simplicity assume that future returns are received at the end of each year. Present values are calculated for 2 discount rates (d), 10% and 20%.

		Cost of project incurred at the start of the period £500 000 The project has a life of 5 years	
Return (£)	End of year	Present value	
		d = 10% (£)	d = 20% (£)
20 000	1	18 182	16 667
130 000	2	107 438	90 278
260 000	3	195 342	150 463
240 000	4	163 923	115 741
50 000	5	31 046	20 094
	Total	515 931	393 243

The **net present value** of the project at a constant discount rate of 10% is £15 931 but at a constant rate of 20% it is – £106 757. Discounted at 20% the project is showing a negative net present value, i.e. a loss. At some rate between 10% and 20% the net present value must be zero. In fact this rate is 11.1%, calculated from a computer program.

A simple graph (shown in Figure 9.1) illustrates the effect of different discount rates and the internal rate of return.

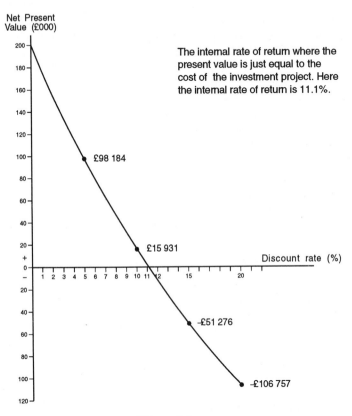

Figure 9.1

Firms using this technique have a target rate of internal rate of return and projects submitted for consideration by the directors, or others having the responsibility for investment decisions, must show an IRR of not less than this target rate. Other things being equal, projects with the highest rates are the ones most likely to be accepted. When setting a target rate, account will be taken of current and anticipated future rates of interest in the financial market, the general economic climate and outlook for the industry or industries in which the company operates and any other factors thought to affect the future prospects for the firm.

Further investment considerations

Investment managers have to take account of many issues related to the costs of obtaining capital for investment and estimating its probable returns. A few important points to bear in mind are the following.

- Funds accumulated within the firm are not costless. If funds are used to finance a project there will be an opportunity cost measured in terms of the lost opportunity to earn an income by investing the funds outside the firm.
- If money is borrowed from the finance market the firm has to accept a legal obligation to pay an agreed rate of interest and to repay the money on the date or dates agreed regardless of the company's profits or losses. The more the amount of money borrowed the greater becomes the burden of meeting these obligations. One of the indicators of a company's financial health is its **gearing ratio**, i.e. the ratio of its borrowings to its ordinary share capital (equity). The higher this gearing ratio the greater the risk of falling victim to a steep rise in interest rates or to a sudden collapse in sales revenue. A number of large retail stores were caught in this trap in the years 1989–91
- Choices often have to be made between projects, each of which, considered individually, is attractive. The choice is rarely just a matter of mathematics. All the appraisal techniques outlined in this unit will provide useful guides but it may be that some projects are competing for the same physical resources such as land or specialist staff or managers while others are dependent on each other, e.g. project A has a better chance of success if project B is also undertaken. Investment decisions should also form part of the firm's overall strategy. An otherwise profitable project may be rejected if it seems likely to divert resources away from the path that senior management wishes to follow in the long term.

Risks and uncertainties of investment

Most investment decisions involve comparing a known amount of expenditure with uncertain receipts in the future. No one can be sure what will happen in the future but decisions still have to be made. Managers can reduce the risks arising from uncertainty by obtaining reliable information about probable future trends, by influencing these trends and by developing techniques to estimate and allow for the degree of uncertainty that has to be faced. Uncertainties for most business activities arise from the market and from the actions of governments.

Seeking information

- Information about markets, particularly about estimated future demand for products is gained from market research as outlined in Unit 7. It is always tempting to concentrate on the techniques of investment appraisal but you should always remember that the success of any investment project depends on the accuracy of forecasts of future sales. Probably the most important part of any appraisal is the market research on which demand forecasts are based. It is also, of course, important to know what market rivals are doing and planning.
- Information about future government actions likely to affect the firm comes from an understanding of economic trends, of the various economic policy options available to governments and of the opinions of civil servants, ministers and shadow ministers in relation to those options. Chief executives of major public companies and their staffs now pay considerable attention to studying political developments and the political actors in the theatres where the companies operate. Former ministers and civil servants are recruited by firms eager to acquire inside knowledge of the machinery of political decision-making and opinion-forming.

Exerting influence

It is a very short step from seeking information to exerting influence.

- Market research is closely linked to advertising and product promotion aimed at ensuring that demand predictions are fulfilled. The same contacts developed to find out what senior civil servants are thinking and how they make decisions, are used to influence those thoughts and decisions.
- One of the benefits of systematic market research linked to investment appraisal is the identification of events likely to alter future events. Where future demand seems sure to hinge on the outcome of these events managers can estimate the degrees of probability for the various possible outcomes. Probabilities can then be assigned to a range of estimates for future sales figures. It will then be possible to estimate a figure which takes into account these probabilities. To take a simple example, if there is a 40% chance that sales will be at a level of 300 units per week in a year's time, a 50% chance they will reach 400 units and a 10% chance they will be 500 units per week then, applying these probabilities produces an estimate of 370 units per week arrived at by summing 300 x 0.4 (= 120), 400 x 0.5 (= 200) and 500 x 0.1 (= 50). Assessing probabilities is a matter of judgement based on the possession of reliable information.

Residual uncertainty and risk

However careful and well informed the forecast the future remains uncertain. In the above example there is still a 40% chance that the estimate of 370 units per week will not be reached. In all cases there is the chance of something totally unforeseen taking place. In periods of high uncertainty such as international political tension, or major economic recession, these risks are increased. To counter the residual uncertainty remaining when the probability of the foreseeable has been taken into account firms may scale down estimates of future returns and/or reduce the period within which projects are expected to achieve their profit targets. The greater the degree of uncertainty the greater the preference for projects expected to pay for themselves in a relatively short time and the greater the reluctance to consider projects whose returns are only expected in the more distant future.

A simple way to achieve this reduction in the time span of acceptable projects is to shorten the target payback period. Much the same result is achieved by raising the target internal rate of return. Whenever decisions are based on internal rates of return there is an inevitable bias towards projects whose returns are expected early in the life of the project. Consider the following comparison of two projects, A and B, each costing an initial £100 000.

Return at end of year	Project A (£)	Project B (£)
1	£10 000	£40 000
2	£20 000	£35 000
3	£45 000	£30 000
4	£55 000	£25 000
5	£40 000	£20 000
Total	£170 000	£150 000

A computer program provided figures for the following table

	Project A	Project B
Simple payback period	3.45 years	2.83 years
IRR	16.6%	17.42%
NPV discount rate		
5%	£43 100	£32 000
10%	£21 800	£17 300
15%	£4 700	£5 200
20%	– £9 100	– £4 900

On the basis of both the simple payback period and internal rate of return, project B would be preferred. However, on discount rates of 5% and 10% project A would be preferred. This situation is illustrated in the graph of Figure 9.2.

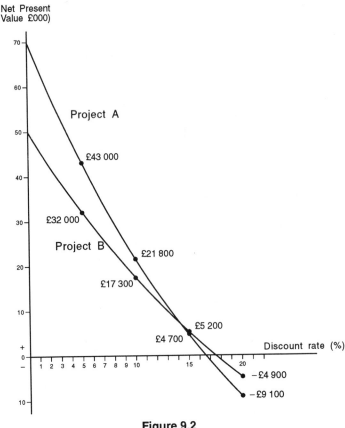

Figure 9.2

If project B is chosen in preference to A, the preference is being exercised in favour of the returns which come early in the life of the project. This is logical if it is believed that these returns can be re-invested more profitably in some other project than project A or if it is believed that long-term investment is too uncertain. If interest rates were likely to fall or if the economic and political climate appeared to be stable the choice of B might not be such a rational choice. Notice that no account is being taken of possible earnings after the five-year period. Project A might be capable of securing significant returns for several more years while B was clearly in decline. There have been many accusations that British and American companies have been reluctant to take a long-term view of investment — in supposed contrast to their German and Japanese competitors. The acknowledged willingness to use IRR as the basis for investment decisions does appear to lend some support to these accusations.

Risk aversion and risk taking

Not all managements take the same view of risk. Differences in attitudes to risks are widely acknowledged and attempts have been made to measure these. Suppose two managers were faced with the same investment decision. They are presented with the same background of uncertainty and the same facts about the project. They agree a suitable discount rate. They are then asked to decide whether or not to accept a project costing an initial £100 000 with an NPV of £10 000. One manager signifies acceptance because the NPV is positive. The other rejects the proposal because the degree of residual uncertainty is too great to justify risking the £100 000 in order to gain just £10 000. This manager argues that the risk should only be taken for an estimated net return of £20 000 or above. The implication is that a **certain** £100 000 can only be equated with an **uncertain** £120 000.

These managers would be showing different attitudes to risk taking. These differences can be found in almost all groups of people. One person in a group crosses a busy road when others hang back waiting for a larger gap in the traffic. One stresses the potential gain from a venture. Another stresses the potential loss. Those who are most likely to base their decisions on the possibilities of losing are termed **risk averters**. Those with their eyes fixed on the potential gains are **risk takers**. Risk averters will tend to prefer projects with the lowest possible losses. Risk takers are more likely to accept projects with the largest potential profits even though they may also carry the largest potential risks of loss.

There is room in business for both attitudes though we might argue that it is preferable for those who trust their money to the management of others should know whether the managers are likely to be risk takers or not. We might also expect financial institutions such as banks and life and pensions offices, whose business it is to lend money belonging to others, to be managed by risk averters. Taking risks with other people's money is rather different from risking one's own. Perhaps those executives of public companies who negotiate profit-sharing schemes should also be required to accept a parallel loss-sharing arrangement!

Discussion and revision questions

- What effect would you expect a high rate of inflation to have on the volume of business investment?

- How far do you think it is possible to apply the appraisal techniques introduced in this unit to investment in human capital?

- What are the advantages and disadvantages of the simple payback and discounted payback methods of investment appraisal?

- Academics are said to favour judging investment projects on the basis of net present values. Business managers are said to favour using the internal rate of return. Suggest reasons for this.

- Show how the use of internal rate of return as the basis for investment appraisal favours projects bringing quick returns.

- Prepare two tables of present values for a constant amount of £5000 payable from 1 to 5 years discounted at 8% and 14%.

- Calculate the net present values (discount rate 12%) and internal rates of return for the following competing projects. Comment on your results. Assume that all net returns are received at the end of the year. If you do not have access to a computer investment appraisal program estimate approximate internal rates of return.

	Project A	Project B
Cost at start	**£100 000**	**£100 000**
Return year 1	£15 000	£35 000
Return year 2	£20 000	£40 000
Return year 3	£35 000	£45 000
Return year 4	£55 000	£25 000
Return year 5	£50 000	£10 000

- All investment is said to be a gamble. Is this still true given the nature of modern computers and computer software packages?

- Outline and discuss the various methods employed by business managers to cope with the uncertainties of business investment.

- Given the impossibility of removing all uncertainty what modifications would you make to the statement that 'A profit maximising firm should accept investment projects when appraisal indicates a positive net present value'.

- Discuss the possible approaches to comparing the following two competing investment projects each requiring an initial investment of £500 000. Assume that the appropriate discount rate is not an issue.

Project	Estimated NPV	Maximum possible loss
A	£50 000	£20 000
B	£150 000	£100 000

Multiple choice questions

The following key applies to the first FIVE questions

A   1 only is correct
B   1 and 2 only are correct
C   1, 2 and 3 are correct
D   2 and 3 only are correct

- Discounting future returns to their present values is desirable in investment appraisal because

  1   all investment is a gamble
  2   money often loses its purchasing power
  3   money can earn an income over time

- The payback method is a widely known and practised method of appraising investment projects because it is

  1   an inexpensive way of investigating projects before more expensive methods are employed
  2   simple to use and easy for non financial managers to understand
  3   an accurate way to ensure that only profitable investments are undertaken

- The choice of a discount rate or rates to be used for discounting future returns should reflect

  1   the cost of capital over the lifetime of the project
  2   estimates of future economic and political uncertainty
  3   the internal rate of return for the project

- When internal rate of return is used to rank competing investment projects we can expect the appraisal to favour those projects which

  1   have the shortest payback periods
  2   have the lowest initial costs
  3   minimise the project's opportunity costs

- If the present value of a future payment of £2000 due to be paid at the end of two years is £1653 (approx) the rate of discount used for discounting the payment is

  A   12.1%
  B   20.1%
  C   10.0%
  D   17.35%

- Projects which take a relatively long time to achieve profitable returns are more likely to be undertaken when

  A deposits with financial institutions earn high rates of interest
  B deposits with financial institutions earn low rates of interest
  C the current economic outlook is perceived to be uncertain
  D business managers replace subjective judgement with discounting appraisal techniques

- When a firm is using its own accumulated profits for investment it should

  A ignore market rates of interest in its appraisal of projects
  B employ discount rates or target IRRs which reflect financial opportunity costs
  C aim at attaining the highest possible gearing ratio
  D increase dividends to shareholders to compensate for the dilution of their capital

- An investment manager, known to favour risk minimisation, is asked to choose one from the following list of available investment projects of roughly equal initial cost and projected profitable life. Which one of the following is the manager most likely to select? The probabilities shown relate to the most optimistic and pessimistic estimates. The appraisal calculations indicate

  A has a 70% chance of earning £200 000 and 20% chance of losing £100 000
  B has a 50% chance of earning £300 000 and 25% chance of losing £80 000
  C has a 65% chance of earning £150 000 and 15% chance of losing £20 000
  D has a 80% chance of earning £250 000 and 15% chance of losing £100 000

- An investment project costing £100 000 is estimated to offer the following undiscounted net returns:

  End of year 1   £25 000
  End of year 2   £50 000
  End of year 3   £60 000
  End of year 4   £40 000

  The approximate internal rate of return is:

  A 75%
  B 25%
  C 19%
  D 30%

10

The firm and financial markets

Topic summary

The firm's needs for finance

It may seem strange that even profitable and successful firms should need additional finance but a closer look at the normal pattern of business activity reveals that most firms at some time or other are likely to experience this need.

Firms financial requirements can be classified in three broad categories.

Short-term finance

There is usually a time gap between receiving an order and payment from the buyer. In the meantime the goods ordered have to be manufactured or obtained from elsewhere. This all involves expense. Workers have to be paid, rents for premises paid, costs incurred for heat, light and telephones and so on. Short-term finance to cover this period is required not only when the firm is starting in business or commencing a new activity but also when it is expanding because the costs of expansion may be greater than can be met from the revenue receipts from a smaller volume of sales.

Medium-term finance

When the firm wishes to acquire equipment either for expansion or to change its production methods it may again require finance and hope to meet its additional costs from the extra revenue that the equipment will help to generate. Again, however, the finance is likely to be needed before the revenue is received. Because the equipment is likely to have a lifetime of several years the firm will also usually hope to spread the financial cost over some years, perhaps three or four and even more in some cases. In these circumstances it needs medium-term finance. Some forms of production, including the manufacture of large pieces of machinery or construction projects may also spread over several years, giving rise to a need for finance over the relevant period.

Long-term and permanent finance

Major expansion or major changes in production method involving substantial reconstruction will need to be financed over a long term. The cost of a new factory is unlikely to be recovered in two or three years. The firm may need finance over a much longer period of ten, fifteen, twenty or more years. Some finance may be obtained on a permanent basis, i.e. the firm has the use of the money for as long as it remains in existence, in return for some kind of share of the profits of the enterprise.

These three broad types of finance have led to the development of their own specialised markets each with its own specialised characteristics and, to some degree, to its own specialised institutions. In practice, of course, the divisions between the three markets are not always clear cut. Short-term finance, for example, may be needed while the firm waits for a favourable time to obtain money from the long-term market. Nevertheless it is important for the distinctions to be kept clearly in mind. Firms which finance long-term expansion with short-term loans are extremely vulnerable to any change in the economic climate leading to demands to repay money that can only be raised from the sale of assets that are essential to the firm's future. A transport company, for example, cannot survive for long if it has to start selling vehicles needed to meet current demand.

The market for short-term finance

Improving cash flow

It should first be recognised that many firms can improve their access to money available to make payments (liquid finance) by systematic reorganisation of their pattern of sales receipts and payments for purchases. Others can improve their stock of liquid finance by paying more careful attention to the inward flow of funds, by, for example, tighter credit control, ensuring prompt payment by debtors. Most people are aware of the term 'cash flow'. Efficient office administration and ensuring that, as far as possible commitments to make payments occur when funds are available to make these payments can reduce the level of short-term borrowing or ensure that money is only borrowed for profitable use.

Trade credit

Credit oils the wheels of business. Most business people wish to see the goods or receive the services they are buying before paying. Preferably they wish to have time to re-sell some of the goods and make use of the services before having to pay. Consequently allowing time to pay is standard trading conduct. Some firms, however, seek to extend this practice by lengthening the credit period so that effectively the buyer is trading on the finances of the seller. Credit, of course, has become part of the competitive process. If the seller allows a buyer longer to pay this is a kind of price reduction because the buyer is being allowed to use the money to earn income during the extended period. Many managers regard trade credit as a free loan. In contrast, accountants point out that trade credit beyond the business norm almost always incurs a cost. If firms know that a buyer is going to take extended credit some will be reluctant to trade and probably quote prices that are deliberately uncompetitive. Others will raise prices or reduce the quality of service in compensation. Because few suppliers seek the business of a known late payer that buyer's market power is diminished and with it the ability to secure competitive purchase terms. Some estimates of the true cost of extended trade credit are very high.

Short-term borrowing

Firms which are fundamentally financially sound can usually obtain finance from the banking system in one form or another. The precise manner in which this is arranged depends on their own circumstances, the nature of their activities and the security they can offer to guarantee that the loans can be repaid and interest charges met.

- **Overdrafts**

  Banks recognise that profitable firms may not wish to have money lying idle in bank balances and will trade up to the limit of their available cash. This creates a danger of miscalculation or the cash being used up if inward payments are unexpectedly delayed. Most firms, therefore, and indeed most individuals, are able to arrange an overdraft facility with their bank so that cheques drawn on their accounts will be paid, up to an agreed limit above their account balances. Overdrafts have always been recognised as an extremely flexible and convenient method of borrowing with interest charged on a daily basis on the amount actually overdrawn. In recent years, however, banks have sought to raise the cost of overdrafts by making charges not faced by customers who keep credit balances in their accounts. They have also become more reluctant to permit the constant renewal of substantial overdrafts to firms using them as virtual permanent capital. Much depends on the relationship between bank and customer and the nature of the firm's business. If the firm is trading in readily saleable stock, subject to constant and steady turnover and does not have too many other claims on its assets then a semi-permanent overdraft can often be permitted in safety. Nevertheless, one of the lessons of the recession of 1990–1 was that not all retail stocks fell into this category.

- **Loans**

  Where possible, particularly with small businesses, banks are likely to insist on fixed terms and repayment of the loan by instalments during the agreed term. Of course banks are not the only source of loans but they are the most common. Many firms are able to borrow from other organisations or individuals on mutually agreed conditions.

- **Factoring**

  In the financial world a factor is an institution, usually a subsidiary of a bank, which takes over agreed financial responsibilities and obligations on behalf of a client. The factor, in effect, purchases invoices representing debts owed to the business by its customers. The factor usually pays 75 per cent or 80 per cent of the value of the invoices immediately with the balance being paid, less charges, when the invoice is paid by the debtor. The factor administers the sales ledger and accounts collections. In some cases the factor provides credit protection so that, if any debt remains unpaid, the factor will pay, thus protecting the business from the risk of bad debts. Where credit protection is not provided the factor has to make good any payments not collected after a period of three to four months.

  A factor is often able to provide considerably more funds than can be obtained from other forms of borrowing from a bank. This is because security for the funds lies primarily on repayment from a wide spread of debtors rather than from a single business. Before taking on a firm's debts a factor will make credit assessments of the debtors and will normally expect all invoices to be factored.

- **Invoice discounting**

  This is similar to factoring in that the finance company purchases invoices from the client. However, the sales ledger administration and collection of accounts is carried out by the client. Technically the client administers these as agent for the finance company which must, of course, be fully satisfied that these financial duties are carried out to a high standard and that the client can be fully trusted to handle the debts.

  In some cases the debtors are aware of the discounting agreement. In others, the invoice discounting agreement is confidential. Charges for invoice discounting are lower than for factoring because the finance company does not handle the physical work of accounts collection.

The market for medium-term finance

Finance is often needed for acquiring machines, vehicles or other equipment. The firm hopes that the additional equipment will generate sufficient extra revenue to meet the cost of borrowing and add to profits. It may be possible to arrange loans from banks or other institutions for this purpose but most banks regard this kind of lending as a specialised activity for which they keep specialised subsidiary companies. The security for the finance is clearly the equipment to be acquired and the lender will usually seek to retain ownership rights until the loan is repaid. Most finance is made available under hire purchase or leasing agreements. Taxation rules tend to favour leasing for business purposes but for other purposes there is little practical difference between the two. The consumer protection laws allowing rights of repudiation within a limited period of entering an agreement and restricting the lender's rights of recovery once a third of the total purchase price has been paid, do not apply to corporate borrowers (limited companies) but do apply to individual sole traders and partners.

In most hire purchase and leasing arrangements ownership of the property passes to the borrower with the final payment but it is sometimes possible to hire or lease equipment with no right of purchase. This is not strictly borrowing but it is a method of acquiring equipment without having to make a large capital payment before obtaining any benefit from its use and is a form of finance available to firms which consider it meets their needs.

The capital market for long-term and permanent finance

Retention of revenue

Most firms plough back a proportion of their profits into long-term investment. Many aim to re-invest around a half of their after-tax profits. This, of course, is not 'free money'. There is an opportunity cost in the form of the interest that could be earned if the funds were invested outside the business so that the same careful appraisal methods are needed for re-investing profits as for raising funds from outside sources.

Profits retained in the business are not being distributed to shareholders as dividend. Any holding back on dividend has a potential effect on the value of the company's shares. Ignoring the effects of short-term speculation and of take-over bids the true market value of a company's ordinary share is the discounted value of the anticipated stream of future dividends it is expected to earn. A company known to favour reinvestment at the expense of dividends will not enjoy a high market valuation for its shares. On the other hand, maintaining high current dividends at the cost of failing to invest and so limiting prospects of future growth for the company and its dividends, will also depress share values. Consequently the directors have to adopt a policy which avoids the two extremes of meanness and over generosity to shareholders. Given a choice between using retained profits and raising money from the capital market investment managers can be expected to opt for profits as they may then avoid detailed scrutiny of their intentions by external analysts employed to advise potential sources of funds. Whether this is desirable in the long-term interests of the company and its shareholders is less certain.

Borrowing

- **Long-term loans**

Firms may seek long-term (periods of five years or more) loans from banks or other institutions prepared to make this kind of finance available. The problem for the firm is that it is committed to interest payments for the full term regardless of its profit performance. Lenders take the risk that interest rates agreed at the start of the loan may underestimate future inflation rates and result in negative returns if high rates of price increases actually exceed the interest rate. To avoid this risk they will either demand very high rates or seek to link interest payable to bank base rates so that they are protected to some extent against inflation and rising interest rates. However, such protection is ineffective if a rising interest payment burden pushes a company into financial difficulties to the extent that the lender has to choose between easing the burden or pushing the firm into liquidation with the possible loss of the entire loan.

- **Finance from land or property ownership**

Those firms owning land or property can usually use it as security to obtain finance. One method is through a **mortgage** whereby the lender becomes the legal owner of property mortgaged but the borrower enjoys its possession and use and many of the practical benefits of ownership — **as long as the terms of the mortgage are not broken.** Any failure to pay the agreed interest charge or make an agreed repayment of capital can result in the lender taking possession of the property.

Another method is through **sale and leaseback.** Here the firm sells the freehold of its land or property to a financial institution under an agreement whereby it leases it back over a long period with provision for periodic rent reviews. The firm is able to invest the finance from the sale of the property which it continues to occupy. The finance house gains an annual income from rent plus any increase in the value of the property.

- **Bonds**

Companies can issue bonds in the form of debentures or loan stocks which can be sold in much the same way as ordinary shares. These stocks pay a fixed rate of interest and are repayable at stated dates. In periods of inflation there is a natural reluctance for people to buy such stocks because the fixed rate of interest may diminish in value as market rates of interest rise. Stocks also lose their purchasing power through continued inflation. When inflation is present or anticipated fixed interest stocks can only be issued at very high interest rates. Companies are reluctant to agree to these so they are only likely to be used on a significant scale when inflation rates are low and expected to stay low in the foreseeable future.

Ordinary Shares

A share gets its name because it literally represents a share of the common or joint stock of capital that is provided by the people who form the company. This capital, for example, might be made up of £1 000 000 divided into one million shares of £1 each. Individuals, organisations or other companies can hold as few or as many shares as they wish and can afford to buy. Each share conveys to its holder the right to cast one vote at shareholders' meetings so that full control of the company is in the hands of holders of 51% of the shares.

Holders of shares may sell them to whoever is willing to buy at a price which will reflect views of how profitable the firm is likely to be in the future. Only if the company fulfils the statutory requirements for recognition as a public company can its shares and debenture or loan stocks be advertised for sale to the public. Private company shares can only be traded by private arrangements. Most public company shares in Britain are traded in one of the two markets for shares which form the International Stock Exchange operating in London and a number of other cities in the United Kingdom and Ireland. These two markets are the Main Market for securities held in the Official List (the listed market) and the Unlisted Securities Market (the USM).

When a company is formed or extends its capital by issuing new shares these pass through the New Issue Market which is controlled by the institutions of the Stock Exchange. Money from the sale of entirely new shares goes to the company for investment. Once issued, shares are traded in the Stock Exchange and money simply passes from buyer to seller, via their broker agents. The company does not receive any further money as its shares are traded nor does it gain directly from any increase in its share value. However, most managers like to see the market value of their companies' shares rising because this makes it easier for them to issue more new shares, makes take over more expensive and thus, less likely, and indicates that they have the approval of the financial institutions whose support is essential to any company wishing to raise investment capital. Investors also like to see share prices rising because this makes it more likely that they can re-sell shares at a profit and increases the popularity of share ownership.

When a company expands its capital and raises finance by issuing additional shares it is normally required to offer them first to its existing shareholders at a favourable price. Each existing shareholder is given the **right** to buy a certain number of shares depending on the number currently held. Shareholders not wishing to take up these rights can sell them through the stock exchange. This recognises that an increase in the number of shares **dilutes** the value of existing shares because profits then have to be divided into more shares. Companies, of course, claim that the additional finance will enable the company to increase profits so that future dividends will increase. There can be no guarantee that this will happen.

Preference shares and convertibles

By far the majority of shares are ordinary shares but variations have been introduced from time to time, usually to try and combine the benefits of having a known dividend or interest income and permitting some of the advantages of the ordinary share with its possibilities for growth in dividend and capital value.

- **Preference shares**
  As their name implies, these give some degree of preference to their holders over ordinary shareholders in rights to receive a dividend which, however, is limited to a stated percentage of the nominal value of the share. In periods of inflation relatively few are issued because of the decline in the value of the fixed dividend when prices and the returns on most other financial securities are rising.

- **Convertible Stocks**
  These are fixed interest loan stocks which carry the right of conversion to ordinary shares at a fixed price within given dates. Their market value depends partly on current market rates of interest and partly on the value of the company's ordinary shares.

Institutions of the finance markets

The banks

Although the distinctions between short–, medium– and long–term finance are clear and there are distinct divisions between their respective markets institutions may operate in more than one of the markets. The major High Street banks are involved directly and indirectly in all the finance markets. They operate in the very short term interbank and Money market, extend overdraft and loan facilities for short, medium and long terms and may purchase debentures and loan stocks if they feel this is justified. They also own or help to finance many specialised subsidiaries such as factors, leasing and hire purchase companies. In the face of competition from the building societies they have invaded building society territory by providing house purchase finance and, since the Stock Exchange changes of 1986 they have taken a more active part in the capital market.

The merchant banks, some of which are owned or controlled by the High Street Banks operate mainly in the wholesale finance markets, dealing in very large sums of money and advising the large and growing business firms in such matters as take overs, financial management and the arrangement of finance through the capital market. Those with new issue departments arrange issues of shares and loan stocks. The larger merchant banks operate internationally through most of the major world finance markets.

The Stock Exchange

The centre of the capital market is the Stock Exchange whose main activities were outlined in the previous section. In an economy dependent upon private capital an efficient stock exchange is essential to both the public and the private sectors. Few could afford to make money available to the government or to business organisations for their long term or permanent use unless there were some system for recovering cash at short notice. The ability to trade securities and thus convert shares and stocks into cash without requiring any repayment from the government or business companies enables the community to make full use of available finance without having to keep large amounts available for repayment on demand. A stock exchange also enables ordinary individuals with modest savings to share in the profits and risks of business enterprise with a greater degree of safety and protection than is possible when people lend money to business outside an organised market system. Unit and investment trusts provide further means of making savings available to business without running the risk of losing all in the event of a single business failure.

It is sometimes argued that there should be greater safeguards to protect companies from take-over on the grounds that it is wrong for people's jobs, in effect, to be bought and sold by shareholders in the interest of profit. However, there is a powerful argument that an unregulated capital market ensures that a company making inefficient use of resources and hence low profits, is very likely to be taken over by a more efficient company able to make more profitable use of resources. This suggests that an unregulated capital market with few restrictions on take-overs fulfils an economic function in ensuring the efficient use of scarce resources. Management skills are among these scarce resources and it is likely to be the less effective managerial teams that fall victim to take-over by the more competent and effective. This, of course, does raise some controversial issues which you may wish to consider and discuss.

It should never be forgotten that all business activity involves risks. The stock exchange tends to gain its greatest publicity and to appear at its most glamorous when the economy is booming and everyone seems to be making easy profits. Investment, whether by business firms or private individuals, remains a gamble because no one can foretell the future with accuracy. Money is lost as well as gained in stock markets.

The non-banking intermediaries

A feature of modern finance markets has been the growth of financial institutions which are not banks and which do not aspire to be banks. Among the most important of these are the insurance offices and the pension funds. Both have gained prominence through the massive expansion in pensions provision for workers of all kinds since the early 1950s.

Pension schemes involve the regular payment of premiums over a long period of time and payment is normally made by firms and is thus more consistent and reliable than payments by private individuals. Mortality tables have been kept over several centuries so life expectancy can be calculated with greater accuracy than, say, the risks of hurricanes. Consequently the pensions offices are able to arrange long-term investments with some confidence though they are not, of course, immune from the risks associated with all investment. Many life assurance offices suffered substantial losses when property values fell sharply at the end of the 1980s. Much of the urban, commercial re-development of the 1960s and 1970s was financed by insurance and pension funds. Many modern shopping precincts were built with pension premiums. The scale of High Street re-development was certainly impressive. Whether the results were entirely desirable is a matter of rather less certainty.

Discussion and revision questions

- A company's investment manager admits to a preference for arranging all the firm's outside finance for investment purposes on a short-term basis on the grounds that long-term financial commitments present too many risks. Discuss the wisdom of this preference.

- 'Neither a borrower nor a lender be.' Is this wise advice for the owner of a business organisation? Justify your answer.

- Suggest reasons why a firm might wish to factor its trade debts but to do this on an undisclosed basis.

- Under what circumstances are borrowers likely to want to arrange fixed interest loans? Under what circumstances are lenders most likely to agree to such loans?

- What is meant when a lender says that it needs security for a loan? How can this security be provided?

- Under what circumstances might firms prefer to hire rather than purchase equipment?

- What are the advantages and the dangers of growth for a company's shareholders?

- The gearing ratio is the ratio of a company's borrowing to its ordinary share capital. If the ratio is considered to be high the company is said to be highly geared. What are the dangers for a company of being highly geared? Why might some people wish to buy shares in a highly geared company?

- Examine the list of share prices in a leading daily journal such as *The Times* or *The Financial Times*. Examine the column showing the **yield** of the shares.

  Explain the meaning of share yield.
  What do you notice about the yields of the various groups of shares?
  Suggest reasons for the yield differences between these groups.

- Discuss the view that preference shares are safer than ordinary shares.

- Why are company managers interested in the stock market prices of their company's shares when dealings in the shares do not affect the amount of the company's capital?

- Only a relatively small proportion of the population is dependent for a significant part of its income on stock exchange investments. Why then should the movement of share prices on the stock exchange be a matter of public interest and concern?

- Discuss the case for allowing banks to form associations designed to limit the amount of inter-bank competition.

- Explain what is meant by a unit trust. Suggest reasons why financial advisers frequently advise small private investors to buy unit trusts and not ordinary shares.

- Discuss the argument that the managers of a company's pension fund should not be permitted to use the fund to buy that company's shares.

Multiple choice questions

The following key applies to the first FIVE questions

A   1 only is correct
B   1 and 2 only are correct
C   1, 2 and 3 are correct
D   2 and 3 are correct

- Valid economic reasons for business companies to use some form of hire purchase or leasing arrangement to acquire equipment include

  1   anticipation that the equipment will earn revenue to meet the costs of the financial arrangement
  2   the desire to use all available capital to develop the business
  3   the security of being able to cease payments at any time by returning goods to the buyer

- Successful firms may require to borrow because

    1   costs are often incurred before the revenue they generate is received
    2   growth implies the need to increase production capacity
    3   buyers often require credit in competitive markets

- Companies planning major expansion may choose to issue additional shares because

    1   shares can be repaid quickly when revenue starts to increase
    2   they do not want to have to sell essential assets to meet short term liabilities
    3   should revenues and profits fall they have greater powers to reduce dividends than interest charges

- The gearing ratios of retail supermarket and grocery companies tend to be higher than those for manufacturers because

    1   retailers trade at a later stage in the chain of production than do manufacturers
    2   retailers can usually raise cash quickly by running down stocks
    3   most established brands of food and groceries enjoy a steady level of demand

- If a company regularly retains a high proportion of its profits for investment its share price is likely to fall because

    1   shareholders feel that this policy is reducing their dividend incomes
    2   there is likely to be a scarcity of the company's shares available for trading in the stock exchange
    3   there will not be enough cash available to pay shareholders who wish to sell their shares

- A stock exchange performs an economic function in a market economy when a rise in share prices

    A   increases the amount of finance that companies can invest
    B   increases the profits of business companies
    C   makes it easier for shareholders to trade their shares
    D   provides finance to increase the wages of employees

- Factoring business debts is a method of speeding a firm's cash flow but factors are unable to reduce

    A   the risk of bad debts
    B   exchange rate risks
    C   office administration costs
    D   marketing costs

- A company will reduce its gearing ratio by

  A   repaying debenture stock and issuing additional ordinary shares
  B   repurchasing ordinary shares and issuing debenture stock
  C   repaying debenture stock and mortgaging its freehold property
  D   repaying bank borrowing with the proceeds of new long term loan stocks

- An unregulated stock exchange provides an economic function in a market economy when

  A   speculation raises share prices
  B   the fear of take over increases managerial efficiency
  C   take-over activity increases share prices
  D   take-over bids are investigated by the Monopolies and Mergers Commission

- A rights issue enables a company immediately to increase

  A   its share capital
  B   its gearing ratio
  C   the value of each of its shares
  D   its sales revenue

11
The firm and the public

Topic summary

Efficiency

At this stage you should revise Unit 5 and make sure you have a sound grasp of the concept of structure, conduct and performance and the market structures of perfect competition, monopoly, monopolistic competition and oligopoly.

Economists have long sought to answer questions concerning people's expectations from an economic system and the kind of market structure most likely to meet those expectations. One expectation is that the system should be efficient. This immediately raises the further question, 'What do we mean by efficiency?'.

There are two main aspects to efficiency. These relate on the one hand to the allocation and on the other to the production of goods and services, i.e. there is **allocative efficiency** and **production (or technical) efficiency**.

Allocative efficiency

This exists when people are receiving those goods and services which they require in the proportions required. It is not being achieved if there are stocks of goods which no one wishes to buy and shortages of other goods which people want to have but cannot find. Nor is it being achieved if there are numbers of empty houses in some parts of a country and homeless people sleeping rough in others. If allocative efficiency is being attained then the scarce economic production factors of land, labour and capital are being directed to those activities most valued by the community in the proportions and to the extent needed to provide the highest possible level of welfare to the community as a whole.

If the highest possible level of allocative efficiency were achieved it would not be possible to divert a single unit of any production factor from one economic activity to another without reducing the total level of satisfaction within the community. It would not be possible to make anyone feel that he or she was better off without making others feel that they were worse off. As long as it remains possible to increase the satisfaction of some without reducing the welfare of others, maximum welfare for the community as a whole is not being achieved.

How then do we measure satisfaction? In a market economy people indicate their valuation of goods and services by their willingness or reluctance to buy them. The value of any good to any particular person is the amount of money that person is willing to pay to obtain it. Assuming that the price ruling in the market is the result of the unregulated and uncontrolled market forces of supply and demand, a good's market price is the visible representation of the value placed on that good by the collective decisions of the community. If we accept this idea then the good's demand curve, representing the prices that people are prepared to pay for different quantity levels of the good, can also be seen as a **social valuation curve**, representing the values placed on the good by society at different levels of availability.

In a pure market economy the resources or production factors are also allocated in markets, and producers wishing to hire them compete with others, so that the resources needed to produce an extra unit of production are obtained at a marginal cost which may be seen as their opportunity cost. This cost represents the community's valuation of the resources for their various possible uses so that the marginal cost curve can be seen as a kind of marginal social cost curve.

Clearly the best output level for any given good from the community's point of view is that level where marginal social cost just equals the community's marginal social valuation. From the assumptions we have made this is also where the marginal cost equals the price. This is illustrated in Figure 11.1.

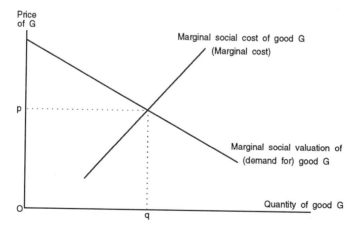

Figure 11.1 The most efficient price and quantity levels for a good G based on allocated efficiency. The community's interests are best served if G is priced at Op and if quantity Oq it produced.

Production (technical) efficiency

Production efficiency is achieved when goods or services are produced with the smallest possible input of production factors i.e. at the lowest possible resource cost with cost measured in physical quantities of resources rather than in money terms. In a world with unlimited wants and scarce resources it is clearly in everyone's interest to obtain the largest possible output of goods and services from available factors, provided that allocative efficiency is also achieved. There is no virtue in producing goods that no one wants.

Economists usually argue that production efficiency is achieved when production takes place on the boundaries of the production frontier. This frontier represents the limits of what can be produced at the current level of technical knowledge. A simple two-dimensional curve is illustrated in Figure 11.2.

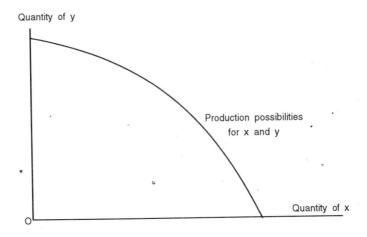

Figure 11.2 At a given level of technology goods x and y can be produced in quantities up to the limit of the curve. If production is at levels within the curve some revenues are not being used. The most efficient levels are on the curve. The best position on the curve depends on the community's valuation of x and y.

What we cannot know is whether this boundary is itself at the limit of what the community as a whole is capable of achieving or whether it is being held under some kind of constraint. It is, of course, possible to compare the production capabilities of particular industries in particular countries and to conclude that one is more productive than the other. The less productive country may then be said to be capable of expanding the boundaries of its production frontier. It is less easy to know whether or not the more productive country is still capable of making more effective use of its technical resources or of speeding the pace of technical advance.

Market structures and efficiency

If we accept the model of structure influencing conduct, influencing performance, outlined at the beginning of Unit 5 we would expect the structure of markets to influence both allocative and production efficiency.

Perfect competition

This is the only unregulated market model which predicts that firms will seek to produce at output levels where marginal cost equals price. It can also be argued that firms operating in perfectly competitive markets will have to produce at their lowest cost levels, i.e. at the limits of their available production frontiers. However, there are powerful arguments to suggest that these frontiers are likely to be severely constrained by the very conditions that are necessary to achieve the perfectly competitive market. In particular we have to recognise:

- The requirement that firms should be small relative to the size of the market so that they are powerless to influence price by their own output decisions is likely to mean that they are also likely to be failing to obtain the full benefits of economies of scale. If firms are producing at output levels below the minimum efficient scale of operations for their industry they are not achieving production efficiency.
- The requirement of perfect communications so that no one firm has any technical superiority over another removes the incentive to search for technical improvements. Self interest is assumed to be the dominating force in market economies and it is not in the self interest of firms to expend resources to acquire knowledge from which they cannot gain competitive advantage because it is immediately shared with their competitors.
- Inability to make profits above the minimum required to keep the firm from leaving the market makes it virtually impossible for any single firm to accumulate the resources needed to undertake research and development work in order to advance production technology.

In simple terms, therefore, perfect competition can be criticised on the grounds that while it may lead to a sharing of the total production cake that maximises community welfare it is also likely to lead to a cake that is smaller than might be achieved under different market conditions.

Perfect competition is commonly criticised for its dependence on assumptions that are themselves somewhat unrealistic. From the point of view of the welfare argument the most serious lack of realism lies in the basic assumption that price represents marginal social valuation. This would only be true if every buyer in the market had equal power to express a preference, i.e. if everyone had the same disposable income. This is patently not the case. Purchasing power is skewed very heavily in favour of a relatively small proportion of the total population. Even if incomes were equal there is no certainty that price would represent a valuation that would be socially acceptable to the community. The proportion of physically disabled people in the community is very small. An unregulated market would probably not choose to allocate sufficient resources to satisfying the needs of the physically disabled on a scale sufficient to permit this group to lead active and fulfilling lives. It is not difficult to find further examples of market deficiencies. Precisely because unregulated markets operate on a basis of self interest they are rarely effective in the provision of public goods. Only when the State started to use its powers to coerce, were standards of sewers, waste disposal, communications, urban lighting and public safety raised to levels where epidemics of killer diseases and the perils of street crime could be brought under control.

Monopoly

If perfect competition is credited with virtues that prove difficult to justify on detailed analysis, monopoly is sometimes greeted with equally undeserved hostility. This is partly the result of circular reasoning. The monopoly model, reproduced in Figure 11.3, assumes that the firm is seeking to maximise profits. On this assumption it is possible to achieve what are often called supernormal profits. It is then frequently suggested that the model 'proves' that the firm maximises profits and achieves unjustifiably high profits.

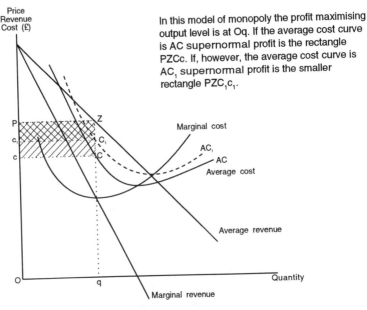

In this model of monopoly the profit maximising output level is at Oq. If the average cost curve is AC supernormal profit is the rectangle PZCc. If, however, the average cost curve is AC_1 supernormal profit is the smaller rectangle PZC_1c_1.

Figure 11.3 Model of monopoly

In fact as indicated in Figure 11.3 there is nothing in the model to indicate what, if any, level of supernormal profit the firm can achieve. This depends on the position of the average cost curve. This, in turn, depends on the level of fixed costs which can only be assumed. It may seem reasonable to believe that firms will not go to the trouble to defend a monopoly position unless they perceive some advantage to themselves in doing so but we hardly need an analytical model to tell us that. Even if we accept this argument we still do not know what advantage is being defended. It may be profit going to the shareholders but as we have indicated earlier in Unit 5, the interests of shareholders may not be dominant. Professional business managers may prefer instead to maximise their own 'perks' (included in general business costs), to protect themselves from the pressures and uncertainties of market competition or to avoid the changes and uncertainties consequent upon technical development.

This brings us to the core of the uncertainties surrounding monopoly power. It is not so much the question of profit or the belief that price will always be above marginal cost. Once we begin to question the profit maximising objective and accept that we cannot predict the position of the average cost curve it is perfectly feasible to bring price and marginal cost together.

The real debate, however, centres on the monopolist's attitude to production efficiency. The two sides of the argument are clear. The monopolist can argue that:

- profit above the perfectly competitive minimum is needed to finance technical research and develop and to provide the incentive to incur the very substantial risks involved in these activities.
- barriers to competition and communication are necessary to secure the benefits of technical development and achieve the size and scale of output needed to secure the economies of large scale operation.

Practices perceived as anti-competitive and against the public interest are thus argued to be in the best interests of the community by advancing the frontiers of production possibilities, and by developing new products and new production technology.

The counter argument suggests that:

- Monopoly erects a barrier against competition behind which managers are freed from any need to pursue change and technical development. Firms which have secured a dominant position in the supply of a product are unlikely to pursue research leading to the replacement of that product by a less profitable substitute. Producers of radio valves did not develop transistors. Manufacturers of mechanical cash registers did not develop computers and electronic tills and the giants of mainframe computer production sought to delay rather than advance early developments in desktop computers.
- Freedom from competitive pressures permits the growth of managerial X-inefficiencies. These arise through the failure to operate at minimum cost or to use resources at their most efficient levels even at the current level of technical knowledge.

This counter argument sees monopoly as the killer of innovation and the enemy of production efficiency.

We have to conclude that economic analysis on its own cannot prove conclusively that either of the market extremes of perfect competition and monopoly can be guaranteed to advance or detract from the sum of public welfare.

Imperfect competition

This term really covers the great number of markets which are between the extremes of perfect competition and monopoly but for most purposes it is sufficient to identify just the two models of monopolistic competition and oligopoly as outlined in Unit 5.

Monopolistic competition

This structure appears to offer little of the assumed welfare benefits of perfect competition. There is no mechanism to bring price into equality with marginal cost but firms are unable to make the monopoly profits which they claim are necessary to the pursuit of technical advance, nor do they gain substantial economies of scale. The text book model suggests that because the average cost curve is still falling at the profit-maximising output level where supernormal profit is competed away and the average cost curve is at a tangent to the average revenue curve, there are unused scarce resources leading to production inefficiency. This is illustrated in Figure 11. 4.

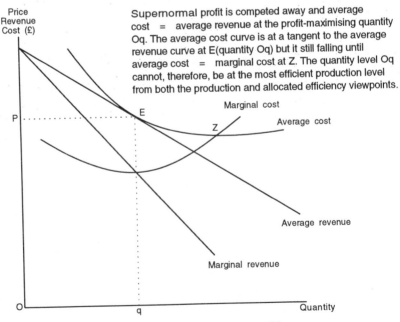

Price Revenue Cost (£)

Supernormal profit is competed away and average cost = average revenue at the profit-maximising quantity Oq. The average cost curve is at a tangent to the average revenue curve at E(quantity Oq) but it still falling until average cost = marginal cost at Z. The quantity level Oq cannot, therefore, be at the most efficient production level from both the production and allocated efficiency viewpoints.

Marginal cost

P

E

Z

Average cost

Average revenue

Marginal revenue

O   q   Quantity

Figure 11.4 Monopolistic competition

The only direct benefit gained by consumers is increased choice between competing products which are no longer perceived as homogeneous. However, they may also gain from the efforts made by suppliers to gain advantages over their rivals. This may lead them to make more efficient use of resources and to pursue technical and marketing innovation. From the suppliers' viewpoint monopolistic competition is an unstable structure of considerable rivalry. Out of this rivalry there will be winners and losers and, as time passes, the market is likely to move closer to oligopoly as the winners gain increased market share.

Oligopoly

Unit 5 explained that there was no all embracing model of monopoly. The kinked demand curve model explains one aspect of behaviour but has no major implications for community welfare. It assumes a profit-maximising objective whereas the same unit showed that oligopolies had the freedom to choose different objectives such as the maximisation of revenue or managerial utility or to pursue multiple objectives as established in the behavioural theory of the firm.

Given the uncertainties surrounding the objectives and behaviour of oligopolies it is not possible to use economic analysis to reach indisputable conclusions concerning the welfare implications of oligopoly. Instead attention tends to concentrate on the conduct of oligopolies and the nature and implications of the rivalry between them.

It is possible to hold conflicting views on the implications of oligopolistic behaviour. We may see this as essentially anti-competitive, defensive of existing market power, opposed to innovation and change and detrimental to consumer welfare, or we may detect a high degree of rivalry and insecurity from which consumers can often derive significant benefits.

Evidence for the anti-competitive argument is often based on such practices as the following:

- **Collusive behaviour**
  There is ample evidence of extensive collusive behaviour before the restrictive trade practices legislation of the 1950s and 1960s. Price-fixing was one of the main activities of trade associations while market-sharing and the policing of artificial barriers against new entrants to markets were also widely practised. It is by no means certain that all these practices have ceased in spite of their illegality. Some almost certainly remain in a number of markets though by the very nature of the issue firm evidence is not easily found. The price similarities of products produced by oligopolies and their reluctance to engage in price competition are frequently cited as evidence of collusion but there are

other possible reasons for this, including the kinked demand curve model, the demand price inelasticities of many consumer products in relatively wealthy market economies and the argument that competition drives prices to a floor level beyond which no further price competition is possible.

- **Barriers against market entry**
  Price can be used to discourage entry where established firms have significant cost advantages over potential new entrants. This enables the established firms to reduce prices when a new entrant appears to levels which such an entrant is likely to find unprofitable. Awareness that this will happen is likely to discourage new firms from seeking entry.

  Heavy advertising, often combined with multiple branding and pricing, raises the costs of entry and reduces its potential rewards. By these means established firms seek to cover all segments of the known market, leaving no gaps to be exploited by newcomers. Consumers, faced with many brands each with slightly different prices, feel that they already have a reasonable product choice and are less inclined to try a genuinely new product simply because it is new. Established suppliers may also use advertising to give an illusion of technical progress, reinforcing the belief that a new entrant is unlikely to offer anything not already being supplied.

  Established suppliers can signal their determination to resist entry by incurring very heavy sunk costs which potential rivals recognise will have to be defended and they may take any opportunity to warn such rivals that they will defend their position. A firm may go out of its way to secure a reputation that it will resist entry at almost any cost in the belief that this reputation will not have to be tested more than once.

  Price discrimination can also operate as an entry barrier. Firms with substantial market power as buyers are recognised to be natural targets for any aspiring new entrant and may also be potential suppliers and rivals themselves should they choose to diversify their existing product range. Such firms are likely to be favoured with prices and levels of service that are calculated to dampen any desire to change their existing buying arrangements.

- **Active rivalry**
  Many of the activities seen as defensive and anti-competitive can also be interpreted as moves to remain competitive in the face of rivalry and potential rivalry. Actions aimed at retaining the support of consumers are likely to be in the interests of consumers. The threat of potential competition may be as potent a force for consumer welfare as actual competition.

Advertising is a reminder that buyers do have a choice. Even if brands tend to originate from just two or three suppliers there will be some differences between the brands in price and quality so that most buyers are able to find the brand that satisfies their own wishes. Oligopolies are often unstable. Although a market may be dominated by the same few companies over a long period the market shares held by rival suppliers can change substantially.

Recognition that potential competition can produce many of the welfare benefits of actual competition has led to the development of concepts to enable this to be analysed more carefully. Markets are now examined in the light of their **contestability**. A fully contestable market is one which new suppliers can enter and leave with no costs of entry or exit, i.e. they do not have to acquire specialised equipment or labour but can bring in production factors from other uses and return them to different uses on exit. A fully contestable market poses such a powerful entry threat that suppliers are only likely to be able to earn normal profits and will have to accept a market price resulting from the pure interplay of market forces. This produces conditions approaching perfect competition and the possibility that price and marginal cost will approach equality — the condition suggested for achieving allocative efficiency. The greater the need for specialised capital and labour the less contestable the market and the greater the power of established firms to control competition and limit entry.

As already indicated, a further curb on producer behaviour is recognition that some buyers have countervailing power and have the resources to enter the market as rival suppliers if they so wished. Existing suppliers have to be careful not to provide incentives for such entry. This puts constraints on the prices they can charge and the profits they can earn and is a powerful stimulus to technical efficiency.

Competition and potential competition between substitute products is often stronger than conventional measures indicate. For example, the market for canned dog food is dominated by two major suppliers but pet owners do not have to buy the canned foods. They may choose fresh, dried or frozen foods or even feed their dogs on their own table scraps. They will only buy canned foods if their prices in relation to the convenience (utility) they offer appears to them to be reasonable in relation to the other options available. The pet food suppliers are well aware of this and modify their pricing and marketing strategies accordingly.

Markets, efficiency and the State

Our review of the various market structures has not led to any specific conclusion that one market structure is more likely to achieve ideal levels of community welfare than the others. This, as will be seen in Unit 12, has important implications for public policies on competition. It is also not possible, on the basis of economic analysis alone, to show conclusively that a market economy is more conducive to a high level of community welfare than a State-regulated economy.

In recent years the governments of the market economies have been ready to lay considerable stress on the virtues of competition as a spur to both production and allocative efficiency. At the same time all the market economies have had to face a growing range of problems which many had thought would be solved by rising material living standards, extended education and increased freedom of choice. The real wages of most workers are at historically high levels but large numbers are unemployed. Housing standards for the majority have been rising steadily but large numbers are visibly homeless. There are beggars on the streets of most of the capital cities of Western Europe. Crime and terrorism are dangers that no one can afford to ignore. Economies with these problems cannot claim to be operating efficiently in either of the two senses identified in this unit.

Clearly there are still major deficiencies in modern market economies. Some basic defects have been identified. The driving force of the market economy is self interest translated into the consumer's desire for want satisfaction and the producer's desire for profit. If a community want is not sufficiently in the self interest of individual consumers it will not, through market forces alone, generate opportunities for profit and the want will not be met by the market. Nor will the market provide the means to satisfy the wants of those who are too small in number or whose incomes are too small to generate profits attractive enough to arouse the interest of competent suppliers. In the absence of provision by the State, representing the interests of the community as a whole, the want will remain unsatisfied. If the unfulfilled want is something of importance to the community, e.g. improved health for people at risk from infectious diseases, improved training for people at risk of becoming unemployable or adequate housing for those unable to provide this for themselves then sooner or later this turns into a problem that no one can ignore, e.g. a dangerous epidemic, large scale unemployment, or rising crime.

The logical remedy for this situation seems to be for the State to become the producer of the unsupplied good and for the State to ensure that resources are provided. While accepting that there is always likely to be a part for the State to play as a provider through the public sector there remains the difficulty of ensuring that State activities also meet the efficiency criteria established for the private sector. How then do we ensure that the public sector achieves production and allocative efficiency?

Economists have attempted to offer solutions based on estimating the marginal social benefit of the activities investigated and relating this to the marginal social (or opportunity) cost of the resources required to provide this benefit. This seems to be a remarkably straightforward solution until we start to try and estimate the actual value of an activity's marginal social benefit. We then face the reality that everyone has different ideas on social valuation. Some would put high value on a new school, others a new road or a new hospital. In the private sector the conflict is resolved by people's willingness or unwillingness to pay the good's price. In the public sector choices have to be made by the political machinery of the State. The problem then becomes a political one of how to devise a mechanism to ensure that the community's preferences are reflected in the production that takes place. If people are unequal in the possession of economic resources they are even more unequal in their access to and ability to make use of the machinery of the State. There is an evident danger that the production achieved by the public sector will simply reflect the attitudes and objectives of those who have the greatest political influence and these are unlikely to be representative of the community as a whole. In practice the public sector finds it more difficult than the private sector to achieve production and allocative efficiency.

The efficiency defects of the public sector in most of the industrial market economies have led to widespread moves to transfer many former public sector activities to the private sector and to the cult of competition as the means to secure efficiency. These issues are examined more fully in a later unit.

Discussion and revision questions

- Discuss the problems of achieving allocative efficiency in the production and distribution of social and environmental services.

- 'Market economies are good at achieving production efficiency and poor at allocative efficiency while planned economies are better at allocating than producing.' Discuss this statement.

- With the help of a suitable diagram explain why price is likely to equal marginal revenue in a perfectly competitive product market where 'normal' profits are being made.

- What is meant by the term 'public good'? Why are public goods not always produced or allocated very efficiently in unregulated markets?

- It is often assumed that competitive markets are preferable to monopolies. Suggest possible arguments for favouring monopolies in certain circumstances over more competitive markets.

- Discuss the view that criticisms of monopoly should concentrate on costs rather than on profits.

- In what ways does monopolistic competition differ from perfect competition. Suggest a contemporary consumer product market that seems to you to be an example of monopolistic competition.

- Use all the means at your disposal to examine one of the following consumer product markets: tea bags; canned cat food; canned fruit. How would you describe the structure of these markets? Discuss the extend and effects of competition and rivalry in these markets.

- How would you justify the involvement of the State in the provision of either health or education services? Suggest possible dangers to community welfare that might arise from State control of these services.

Multiple choice questions

- An economic system will have achieved allocative efficiency when

  A it is producing goods and services to the limits of its technology
  B all its production factors of land, capital and labour are fully employed
  C no one can be better off without making someone else worse off
  D everyone has equal purchasing power in the market place

- In a predominantly market economy price values the utility of the marginal buyer only in those markets which

  A are not monopolies
  B allocate on the basis of price
  C approximate to perfect competition
  D are not subject to price regulation

The following key applies to the next SIX questions

  A 1 only is correct
  B 1 and 2 only are correct
  C 1, 2 and 3 are correct
  D 2 and 3 only are correct

- In economies where wants are unlimited and resources scarce the following features will be present

  1 all economic activities have opportunity and resource costs
  2 social welfare requires all goods and services to be produced at the maximum possible level
  3 all essential services have to be provided by the State

- A market cannot be perfectly competitive unless

  1 its participants are motivated by self interest
  2 its communications are perfect
  3 firms have complete freedom of exit from the market

- A perfectly competitive market is unlikely to achieve full technical efficiency because

  1 firms are small relative to market size
  2 any firm can enter the market regardless of efficiency
  3 firms are under pressure to operate at minimum average cost

- The level of allocative efficiency of a market economy is likely to be reduced by

  1 State control over prices
  2 consumers' income inequalities
  3 producers' market power

- A market which is a true monopoly with only one supplier is likely within that defined market, to have the following features

  1 no close substitutes
  2 an excess of demand over a restricted supply
  3 a demand curve not representing social valuation of the product

- The following arguments can be advanced in defence of monopoly

  1 profits are used to finance research and development
  2 market entry barriers are needed to protect technical advances
  3 the pursuit of profit inspires technical advances and innovation

- It is argued that monopolistic competition leads to unused economic resources because, in the long term, firms

  A are prevented from making above normal profits
  B have to maximise profits in order to survive
  C have to produce at levels where average costs are above their minimum
  D are under pressure to advertise to promote their brand images

- Measures of market concentration are unreliable indicators of the real strength of competition because

  A there is no complete economic model of oligopoly
  B oligopolists may not pursue the objective of profit maximisation
  C large companies may be controlled by managers rather than by their shareholders
  D there can be competition from substitute products in other markets

12

Competition, consumer protection and public policy

Topic summary

Competition and economic analysis

Monopoly and market power

Unit 11 showed that economic analysis cannot prove conclusively that any one market structure is superior to the rest from the point of view of consumer welfare. Nor can economic analysis prove that any one structure is completely detrimental to the consumer interest. Even monopoly, the least popular structure with modern economists, can have some features such as economies of scale, that may benefit consumers. Other features could also be suggested, including the use of profit to finance research and development to improve technical efficiency and the achievement of greater stability of employment. This last was seen as a virtue in the later 1930s after a long period of very high unemployment which some people tended to blame on 'cut-throat competition'.

The logical conclusion is that consumer welfare depends not so much on the market structure as on the behaviour of the firm within the market and this depends on the objectives and attitudes of those controlling the enterprise, its owners or senior managers. Certain market structures may make some attitudes more probable but we cannot be sure of the outcome in all cases. Monopoly, for example, or a collusive oligopoly operating as a shared monopoly, may allow firms to gain sufficient market power to allow managers to pursue objectives and behave in ways detrimental to the consumer interest. Evidence of this could include:

- High prices, possibly combined with restricted output, to ensure a high level of demand relative to supply, i.e. behaviour of the kind frequently predicted on the basis of the profit-maximising monopoly model.
- Limited choice of product and little attention to consumer's preferences with little attempt to find out what those preferences are.

- Low standards of service to consumers restricted to the minimum required by law and often less than required by law, the firm relying on the costs and uncertainties of legal action as well as on consumer ignorance to permit breaches of the law in letter and spirit.
- Little innovation and no significant technical progress, the firm relying on its market power to block innovation from rivals, to avoid the costs of research and development except into marketing superficialities, and to prevent the need for costly investment and staff re-training.
- Low wages and poor working conditions, though the ability of firms to enforce these depends on the condition of the labour market in which they operate. Monopolists and oligopolists in product markets are often in a powerful position to dominate their relevant, specialised labour markets, e.g. in electricity generation, banking, insurance and nursing but this is not always the case. Many of the more modern forms of skilled labour, such as electronic and computer engineering, operate in cross-industry markets in which product monopolists have to compete with other employers to obtain the skilled people they need. The wages paid to these tend then to affect the whole of the wage structure within the firm since it is not possible to have the pay of one group of workers completely out of balance with the pay of other groups within the same organisation.

Competition

If, within the term competition are included potential competition from firms with the resources to enter contestable markets and buyers with the resources to become suppliers, as well as the rivalry of other suppliers in the market, then this can be seen as a powerful force to encourage behaviour beneficial to consumers. Such behaviour may be expected to include those benefits identified as being denied by firms seeking to abuse their market power, such as:

- reasonable prices, allowing normal but not excessive profits to suppliers.
- choice of product with all sectors of the market catered for by suppliers anxious not to leave gaps to be exploited by new entrants.
- high standards of service to customers.
- innovation and technical progress in both production and marketing in the desire to keep ahead of market rivals e.g. the microcomputer was developed commercially by small firms operating in a competitive market and not by the large corporations supplying main-frame computers.
- reasonable wages and satisfactory working conditions for workers since employers will be aware that workers hostile to the firm also tend to be hostile to the firm's customers. On the other hand overpaid workers are often found to be contemptuous of customers.

While competition can provide powerful incentives to provide these benefits they may deny firms the means to achieve them. This struggle to survive in a highly competitive market may indeed bring low prices but may also limit product choice, and reduce profits to levels not capable of supporting research and development and not sufficient to justify the risks of innovation. Moreover, it has always been in the highly competitive trades of clothing, hotels and catering and many areas of retailing that the worst instances of 'sweated labour' (workers receiving very low pay and working in bad, often dangerous conditions) have been chronicled.

Anti-competitive practices

Competition and rivalry can bring benefits to consumers and to the buyers of intermediate products along all the links of the chain of production — but it brings discomfort and risks for business owners, managers and workers. Senior managers may put a brave face on the prospect of increased competition with declarations on the lines of, 'We welcome competition it keeps us on our toes.' However, as any athlete or ballet dancer will confirm it is a great strain to be kept continually on one's toes! Most firms will seek respite from this pressure if at all possible. Monopolies, oligopolies and small firms operating in competitive markets will all seek to reduce competition whenever possible.

Practices seeking to achieve this end could include the following:

- **The take-over of market rivals**
  Present company law permits companies to buy the shares of other companies and there is a competitive capital market. This allows companies to extend their market power by purchasing competitors subject to other constraints examined later in this unit.

- **Formation of cartels**
  Firms, large or small, have, in the past, formed associations with the main purpose of restricting competition by such methods as fixing product prices, fixing discounts or commission rates, limiting entry to local markets to association members and sharing information.

- **Price wars**
  Firms seeking entry to restricted markets and those deemed guilty of breaking association rules have found themselves facing organised price competition wherever they have attempted to trade. Prices have been forced down to loss making levels until the target has withdrawn from the market or agreed to keep to customary rules and practices. Once the threat of competition has been removed the established firms have been able to restore profits without further challenge.

- **Blocking supplies or distribution outlets**
  Large firms or dominant associations have sought to destroy unwanted competition by securing the co-operation from the suppliers of essential

materials or services to block their supply. Suppliers of new products to an established market have tended to meet hostility from established distributors who have refused to stock their product. A determined new entrant with sufficient financial resources may have to establish new distribution channels and/or marketing methods. When Hoover introduced its early vacuum cleaners to Britain it met hostility from contemporary wholesalers and retailers but overcame this by recruiting a force of door-to-door sellers. When later the company gained a dominant position in its market it sought to discourage other entrants with new products.

The flow charts reproduced in Figures 12.1 and 12.2 show the various bodies involved in the regulation of mergers and monopolies and anti-competitive practices and their powers and responsibilities.

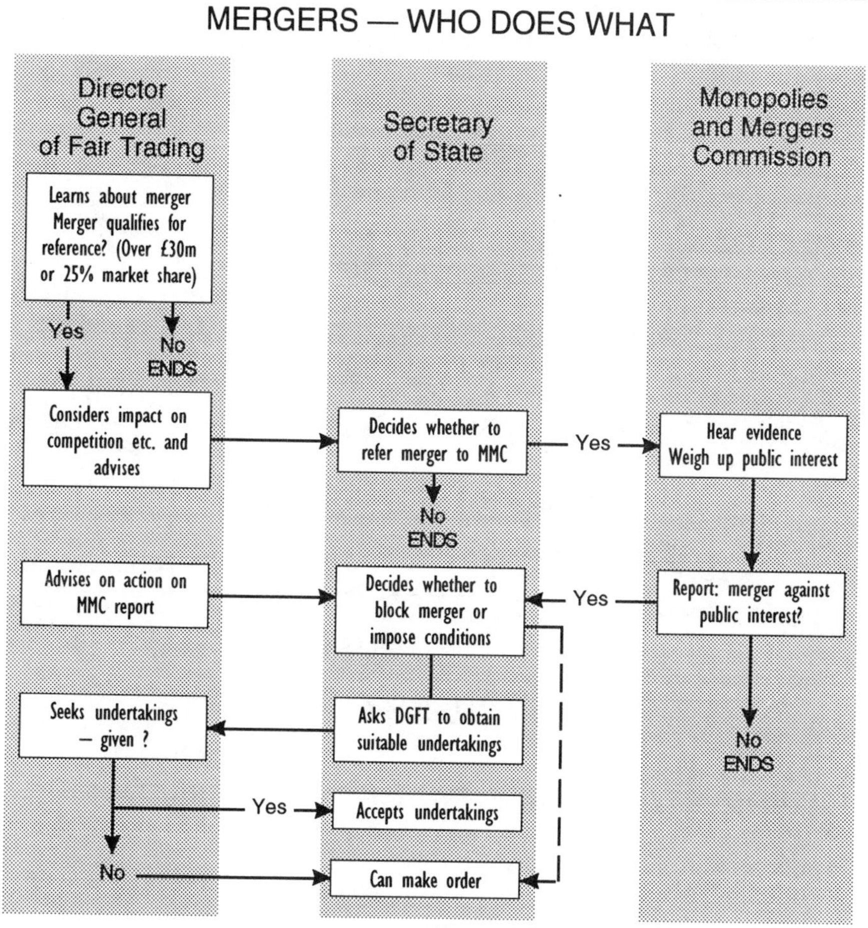

MERGERS — WHO DOES WHAT

Figure 12.1

MONOPOLIES AND ANTI-COMPETITIVE PRACTICES
WHO DOES WHAT

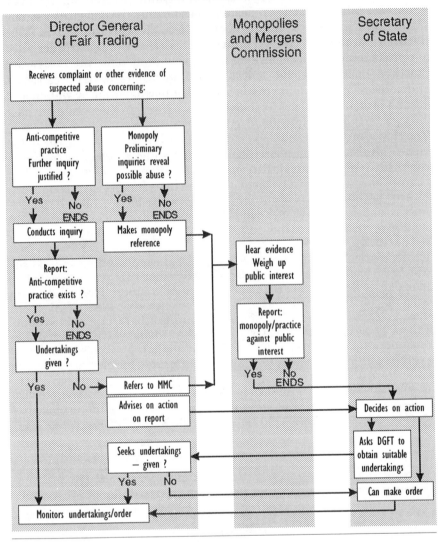

Figure 12.2

Public policy on trading practices and competition

Practices in restraint of trade

No one seriously disputes the fact that freedom from competition or the fear of competition creates opportunities for firms to act in their own interests. The kinds of anti-competitive practices that can develop when firms combine to ensure their survival have been outlined earlier in this unit. In the face of a legal system unable or unwilling to protect individuals against the collective actions of established business organisations strong and wealthy enough to afford lawyers' fees the Government in 1956 started a statutory process to outlaw practices that were clearly designed to restrict competition. It also created a new legal body, the Restrictive Practices Court, with the status of a High Court to 'try' restrictive practices and pronounce verdicts as to whether they were or were not in the public interest, basing its judgement according to their ability to pass through certain clearly defined 'gateways'.

In 1973 the Fair Trading Act, still, in 1991 the leading Act in this area, established an Office and a Director General of Fair Trading and marked a movement away from legal action (though this remained as a last resort) towards negotiation to encourage trade associations to establish codes of practice and set up customer complaints and arbitration procedures with the aim of raising the standards of business practice and customer care.

Self-regulation became the foundation of consumer protection and was the expressed principle of further legislation when this was extended to financial services by the Financial Services Act of 1986. This Act set up a series of subordinate regulatory bodies for each specialised part of the financial services sector. It is sometimes argued that there are too many of these bodies, that their rules are too detailed and restrictive and that consumers are burdened with their high administrative costs. It is always possible to criticise measures to protect consumers but the need for protection is difficult to dispute in a sector where a few unscrupulous people can devour the life's savings of large numbers of innocent individuals. Putting trust in a dishonest finance broker can have more devastating financial consequences than buying a second-hand car from a shady motor dealer.

Monopolies and mergers

Following the same assumption that freedom from competitive pressure permits firms to operate in ways detrimental to consumer interests there has been a further trend to curtail the abuse of market power by:

- investigating the activities of firms which control a large share of a major market and industries where supply is controlled by a few large firms, i.e. oligopolies.
- establishing a filter process to prevent the formation of more or stronger oligopolies where competition could be curtailed.

In Britain, the first element in this trend dates back to 1948 and the formation of the Monopolies and Restrictive Practices Commission, now the Monopolies and Mergers Commission (MMC) operating under the general direction of the Office of Fair Trading (OFT) and the Department for Trade and Industry.

Accepting that there is no economic proof that the mere existence of a monopoly or oligopoly is harmful to public welfare but that they may engage in harmful practices, the basis of British policy is for the Office of Fair Trading to maintain a constant watch on business practices and mergers. Where there is a suspicion that anti-competitive practices exist or where a merger is likely to reduce competition substantially the OFT will advise the Secretary of State for Industry and Trade who may ask the MMC to prepare a report under the provisions of either the Fair Trading Act (1973) or the Competition Act 1980.

In the case of mergers the Companies Act 1989 provides machinery for companies proposing a merger or take-over to consult the Director General for Fair Trading and discover whether it is likely to be allowed or rejected or allowed subject to conditions such as the sale of a subsidiary, to prevent an unacceptable concentration of market power. This allows companies to negotiate with the OFT (and indirectly with the Secretary of State) before commencing a take-over bid and removes the risk of embarking on a costly bid only to have it blocked and referred to the MMC and possibly not permitted.

In practice only a small proportion of mergers where the OFT and Secretary of State have the statutory right to intervene are actually formally investigated by the OFT. A smaller proportion are passed to the MMC for a full investigation and published report and of these only a proportion are completely blocked. Some are permitted subject to undertakings by the companies concerned, the undertakings frequently involve the disposal of companies to prevent an unacceptable limitation of competition.

In recent years the implications for competition have been stated to be the main grounds on which a merger is likely to be questioned.

The European Community dimension

The interest of the European Community in competition arises from Articles 85 and 86 of the Treaty of Rome. Article 85 prohibited most restrictive agreements affecting trade between member countries and Article 86 was concerned with the abuse of market dominance. Until 1990 the Community had little impact on British competition policy though British companies sometimes found it to be one of the barriers against entry to mainland European markets through foreign acquisitions. In September of that year, however, the Commission gained powers, under Merger Control Regulation — Council Regulation 4064/89 — to investigate and pass judgement on mergers with a 'Community dimension'. This was broadly defined as a merger involving organisations with a total world wide turnover over 5 billion ECU (about £3.5 billion at the end of 1990) and where the total Community turnover of at least two of the organisations involved was more than 250 million ECU. Mergers mainly concerning one member of the Community, i.e. where more than two-thirds of the Community turnover of each involved organisations is in one member state only do not come within the regulation which largely supersedes Articles 85 and 86 in so far as these applied to public mergers.

Concentrations with a Community dimension have to be notified to the European Commission within strict time limits of a relevant bid or acquisition of a controlling interest, and merger must not be implemented for at least three weeks after notification, with certain exceptions. The Commission must decide within stated time limits, in most cases, one month, whether the proposed merger is or is not compatible with the common market. It may also negotiate modifications or commitments, e.g. to sell off a part of one of the enterprises, considered necessary to make a merger compatible.

The Commission can also be asked to intervene in mergers which do not have a Community dimension as defined above, but where a member state believes that the merger would result in a significant reduction in competition within this state.

In the short term relatively few mergers are likely to fall within the definition of Community dimension but the number will increase as companies grow larger and as inflation reduces the real size of the 'entry qualification'.

A simplified outline of the procedures under the regulation is shown in Figure 12.3. This whole procedure is intended to be completed within about six to seven months of notification of a proposed merger but this period can be extended if the Commission is unable to obtain the information it needs within the normal time.

Effectiveness of British policies

British competition policy has been criticised both by those who believe it to be weak and ineffectual and by those who regard it as an unnecessary and expensive interference in business affairs.

The arguments for and against stricter controls

Those who argue for stricter controls generally assume that monopolies and oligopolies are, in themselves, a distortion of market forces leading inevitably to the exploitation of consumers and/or workers and to a maldistribution of wealth in favour of those who control large business corporations. Control would, therefore, be based on the banning of concentration limits above stated levels and, where these were already exceeded,

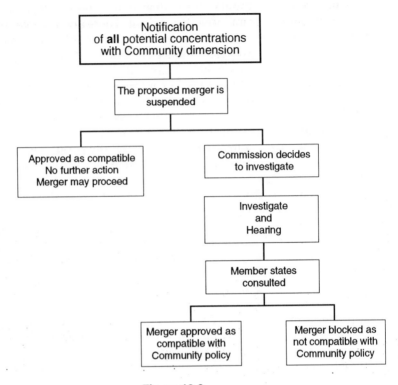

Figure 12.3

on the splitting up of existing business empires. Such a policy, it is claimed would be clearly defined and firms would know precisely what was and what was not permissible. Exceptions to the general rule would be permitted under certain conditions but the onus would be on the firms to show that the public welfare benefit from their monopoly power was greater than the assumed welfare loss from the market concentration. The history of attempts to secure acceptance of restrictive trade practices by the Restrictive Practices Court might suggest that few firms would succeed in becoming exceptions.

This case against statutory controls can be opposed on a number of grounds including:

- The attempt to provide clear legal definitions of market power or even market concentration has the main effect of creating wealth for lawyers. The precise boundaries of any given market and even the definition of a firm, given the complexities of modern finance and management control, present many problems.
- The history of cases judged by the Restrictive Practices Court suggests that uncertainty would remain. It is almost impossible to provide

rational economic explanations to distinguish those agreements which gained acceptance from those that did not. There are possible social and political explanations but if the object of a statutory policy on competition were to be to increase total economic welfare it is more than doubtful whether this would be achieved.

- Lawyers would probably succeed in enforcing the letter of the law — as interpreted by themselves — but large corporations with the financial resources to use the legal machinery would break its spirit and foil its intentions even more effectively because winning a legal battle would enable them to gain effective freedom from any constraints.
- Mergers of smaller firms, without the resources to seek legal loopholes would be prevented and the market power of established, dominant firms would be increased because the threat of effective competition from new and growing firms would be reduced. Economists tend to find that laws passed to secure a specific economic objective, however socially worthy, eventually make that objective harder to achieve in practice because, too often, they ignore or try to reverse powerful, basic, economic forces.
- Competition laws tend to concentrate on horizontal concentration, i.e. control of markets by firms producing similar goods at the same stage of the chain of production, because this is superficially easier to define. Vertical monopoly, i.e. the control of one stage of production by dominating sources of the supply of essential inputs or dominating essential distribution outlets, is apparently more difficult to define or to regulate and tends to be overlooked by legislators. In practice it can be much more effective in limiting genuine competition.

Critics of those who propose statutory policies frequently cite the USA's experience of anti-trust legislation as a warning against moving along this route.

The arguments for and against fewer or no controls

It is sometimes argued that the market is an effective self regulator. If there are opportunities for profitable entry to any market someone will seek entry and awareness that there are always potential entrants as well as actual competitors will influence the behaviour of established producers. In support of this view it can also be argued that:

- Most modern markets are now international so that regulations based on conditions in the domestic market may not take account of the realities of competition from foreign suppliers.
- In a dynamic business environment it is almost impossible to define accurate boundaries for markets as they are perceived by the firms operating in them. New products, materials and technology are constantly changing the challenges faced by suppliers.

- Once regulations are established firms concentrate on meeting their literal requirements without regard to observing their spirit. The introduction of legal rules simply provides work for lawyers and adds to business costs which eventually have to be paid by consumers. Business behaviour does not change to any significant degree. In 1991 BOC (formerly British Oxygen), for example, still dominated the market for industrial gases — a dominance criticised by the Monopolies and Restrictive Practices Commission about 35 years earlier. Aware of its vulnerability to criticism the company tolerated a degree of competition from smaller suppliers but remained sufficiently powerful to prevent this having any significant impact on its activities.

Nevertheless, to remove all forms of regulation and to eliminate the Office of Fair Trading and Monopolies Commission would remove all checks on business conduct. Observation of business behaviour, as well as analysis based on game theory and the economic analysis of duopolies and oligopolies, indicates a strong tendency for firms to collude and make agreements restricting competition if left entirely to themselves. Only the State is powerful enough to oversee their behaviour and to take action to control or modify this if it is considered to be detrimental to the public interest. Economic theory cannot, as yet, identify an ideal market structure. Because there are potential benefits as well as considerable dangers from highly concentrated oligopolies, the British model does seem to offer a workable solution to the problem. This model establishes bodies to observe business behaviour, to compare it with behaviour in other countries, arrange detailed investigations where these seem desirable, and make recommendations for Government action and/or changes in the law where necessary. In Britain in 1991, the Office of Fair Trading was the Department charged with keeping observation on business practices, negotiating reforms and advising government, the Monopolies and Mergers Commission was the investigative body and Government power rested largely with the Secretary of State for Industry and Trade.

It also has to be remembered that, as a member of the European Community, the United Kingdom was also subject to Council Regulation 4064/89, relating to mergers with a 'Community dimension'.

Consumer protection

Development of the law

The idea that consumers need protection against incompetent and/or unscrupulous traders is by no means new. The earliest national consumer protection statute in Britain was enacted in 1238 when standards of fineness for gold and silver were established and these were made easier to police when a decree of 1300 established a system for testing and hall marking items manufactured from gold or silver.

There are well-recorded Medieval local laws relating to standards for food quality and for weights and measures. Traders found guilty of infringing these could face the anger of their customers in the pillory, the Medieval equivalent of certain media investigative reports.

When population sizes were small and most people lived in villages or small towns abuses were checked by the fact that traders had to live with their customers. As population and communities became larger in the nineteenth century abuses became more widespread. Laws were passed to prevent the adulteration of food and to ensure accurate weights and measures but enforcement of these only came with the appointment of the weights and measures inspectorate with powers to enter premises, inspect equipment and generally to ensure that the law was observed. This work is now carried out within the wider consumer protection responsibilities of trading standards officers employed by local authorities.

Local authorities are also responsible for public health through their environmental health departments whose officers are especially concerned with the preparation and sale of food to the public. As practices, technology and materials are constantly changing this is an area where too much detailed legislation could become confusing and unworkable. Modern laws tend to try and balance the need for legislating in some detail on general issues such as food labelling and weighing with the desirability of giving ministers wider powers to take speedy and effective action whenever new abuses are discovered. While the 'front line' work of enforcing the law and also of educating both business firms and the public about consumer safety issues now rests chiefly with consumer protection departments of local authorities the general framework of the law has become the concern of the European Commission. The principle underlying this trend is the belief that a genuinely single market within the European Community can only exist if all firms within the community are subject to the same rules regarding consumer protection.

There are some extreme believers in the virtues of free markets who argue that the market is the best guarantee not only of genuine competition but even for the protection of consumers against harmful and fraudulent practices. Such faith in unregulated markets is based on the principle that if people are free to choose between competing suppliers they will not support firms selling dangerous goods or investment advisers who disappear with their clients' money.

The idea that pressure to secure buyer favour will neutralise the market power of suppliers and ensure that their conduct is not detrimental to buyer interests appears to rest on faith in the underlying honesty and rationality of human beings even greater than the trust placed by extreme socialists in the wisdom and infallibility of decision makers in the command economy. Certainly no one would knowingly pay prices inflated far beyond any reasonable production cost, buy an electric blanket likely to electrocute its user or hand money to an investment advisor known to have a single air ticket to Argentina in his pocket. Unscrupulous, ruthless or power hungry people do not advertise their real intentions. Confidence tricksters act in ways to inspire confidence, not suspicion. It may be true that the dishonest and the incompetent cannot prosper in free markets in the long run but during their run many innocent people can suffer severely. It is not much consolation to the family of a person electrocuted by a faulty electric gadget to know that its supplier will eventually go bankrupt. Individuals and small firms struggling to enter a market dominated by powerful giants need more immediate protection and, when losses are suffered, clear, practical and inexpensive machinery for gaining recompense.

The law on consumer protection has three sources, These are:

- **Common law**
  i.e. the precedents of those previous court cases which were taken to the higher courts and established legal principles to be followed by later courts.

- **Statute law**
  Acts of Parliament, many of which, including the famous Sale of Goods Act 1893, codified and made more accessible precedents established under common law and gave the force of law to practices accepted by business and the community as a whole.

- **European law**
  based on Regulations of the European Commission accepted by the member states of the Community.

Though not having the full force of law considerable reliance is also placed on codes of practice negotiated by the Office of Trading with industry, trade and manufacturer associations. A number of these have set up machinery for handling complaints of customers who have failed to gain satisfaction from suppliers. Members of the associations normally agree to accept the decisions of committees or ombudsmen appointed to settle disputes. Where these exist buyers lose none of their legal rights but usually have a fair and inexpensive means of securing just treatment from suppliers.

The case for consumer protection law

The case for having consumer protection law and for some degree of government involvement to protect consumers as groups or as individuals is based on a number of beliefs.

- Most buyers are likely to have less than perfect knowledge of the goods available in the market or to developments in the wider economy. An individual who buys a new car once every five or more years is unlikely to have the knowledge of a full-time car sales person.
- The normal law as it applies to trade and business is based on the law of contract which, in turn, assumes that parties to agreements enter into them freely and have equal power. In reality individual buyers are far from equal to major international companies which have the resources to take a dispute to the highest possible court, perhaps to discourage the establishment of a precedent which could involve them in considerable increases in costs. Few individuals can afford to risk losing £20 000 in legal fees to recover £1000 lost to a large company. The company is concerned with the possibility of having a thousand or more similar claims and is much more willing to incur costs of, say, £200 000 to avoid the claims.
- The normal legal processes of criminal and civil law in which an aggrieved individual faces a long, daunting and highly expensive series of actions in two sets of courts is unsuitable to the majority of cases involving modest sums of money but where the individual has suffered considerable inconvenience and needs speedy, informal action at low cost.
- Costs are increased and recovery through the normal legal system less likely when the fault lies with firms based in other countries — increasingly likely in modern international markets.
- The fundamental principle of trade practice is 'let the buyer beware', i.e. it is up to buyers to inspect goods, make full enquiries and gain full knowledge before completing a contract and making a payment. Advancing technology makes it virtually impossible to check the safety or effectiveness of electronic goods or the accuracy of brochure descriptions of hotels to be visited on overseas family holidays. The onus of checking can only be changed to a duty to sell safe, effective products conforming to their description by the legislative power of the State.
- Reputable traders have as much to gain from effective consumer protection laws as do customers because their practices are likely to conform to the law anyway and they have an interest in being protected from unscrupulous traders who undercut normal prices by avoiding their responsibilities to customers.

Economics and ethics

In pure economic terms consumer protection law and enforcement machinery are desirable provided that the benefits to consumers are greater than their costs. On this basis it is possible to justify a law enforcing the fitting and wearing of seat belts on the grounds that the savings to the community, e.g. from reduced health service costs and reductions in lost working time and welfare benefits, resulting from fewer injuries and deaths from vehicle accidents are likely to be greater than the costs of enforcing the law and of adding belts to vehicles.

However, this is an area involving moral and ethical principles as well as economic costs and benefits. It might be argued that a reduction in the personal tragedies and human suffering which result from motor vehicle accidents is worthwhile even if the total cost to the community were greater than the total benefit. Some argue that too much regulation in daily activities such as wearing seat belts infringes personal liberties. It would indeed be difficult to defend a complete ban on individual freedom to act dangerously and risk personal injury or death or to force those who chose to take avoidable risks to bear the full consequences themselves without any charge to the rest of the community for health service, welfare, unemployment or other benefits. However, as long as individual actions, however selfish, foolish or misguided, do result in costs and losses for others in the community it does seem just that the community should have a right to regulate activities and to set the boundaries of acceptable conduct. How this is done raises issues which are outside the scope of this text.

Discussion and revision questions

- Outline the main benefits and costs to the consumer of competitive markets.

- 'Simply measuring the concentration ratio of an industry can give a misleading impression of the actual competitive pressures facing firms in that industry.' Explain and discuss this statement.

- 'The only real competition is price competition.' Discuss this statement.

- Discuss the various ways firms can try to reduce the competitive pressures they face.

- To what extent is a high level of advertising evidence of competition in a consumer product market?

- What is meant by 'self-regulation'? Explain how it is put into effect and discuss its effectiveness in relation to any one market familiar to you.

- Read and discuss one Monopolies and Mergers Commission report issued during the past five years.

- Discuss the possible benefits and dangers of extending the part played by the European Commission in controlling monopolies and mergers.

- What criticisms can be made against British competition policy and how might these be answered?

- Discuss the possible consequences of abandoning all controls over monopolies, mergers and restrictive practices.

- Discuss the view that if the British legal system were to adopt the American practice whereby lawyers take on cases in return for a percentage of any financial compensation gained and without charge if nothing was gained, there would be less need of consumer protection because consumers could afford to pursue their normal legal rights.

- In Britain it is compulsory for motorists to insure against the risk of injuring people and for employers to insure against the risk of injuring employees. Should insurance be compulsory for manufacturers of products against the risk of the product injuring a customer?

Multiple choice questions

- State whether the following statements are true (T), false (F) or value judgements (V)

  a In Britain any proposed merger likely to lead to more than 25% of a market coming under the control of one supplier has to be investigated by the Monopolies and Mergers Commission.
  b The main case against monopoly is that it leads to profit maximisation and is thus against the interests of consumers.
  c It is necessary to have a Monopolies and Mergers Commission to discourage further mergers because concentration ratios in British industry are already too high.
  d Competition in product markets benefits consumers through low prices and workers through improved pay and working conditions.
  e Responsibility for regulating merger activity passed from national governments to the European Commission in 1990.
  f It is better for competition policy to be administered by the European Commission rather than by national governments because the Commission will be more objective in its decisions.
  g Since collusion to limit price competition is inevitable in oligopolistic markets the only effective way to restore price competition is to set a legal limit to the concentration ratio permitted in any product market.
  h British consumer protection laws apply only to goods and there is no protection for buyers of services.
  i Firms considering a take-over can consult the Office of Fair Trading before making a bid to discover whether a reference to the Monopolies and Mergers Commission is likely to be made.
  j The final decision whether or not to block a merger rests with the Secretary of State for Trade and Industry.

13

Business location and the community

Topic summary

Business choice of location

Nature of the location decision

Economists and increasingly, geographers, are interested in two broad aspects of business location. They accept that to some degree where firms, and to some extent, industries start can be accidental. Some firms have developed in particular areas because these were the home localities of their founders. This is why Pilkingtons began in St Helens and Morris Motors (later Austin-Morris, British Leyland, BL and Rover Group) began in Oxford. Nevertheless, we need to understand why particular firms and industries appear to have had a greater chance of successful development in some areas as opposed to others.

At the same time we also need to examine the reasons why established firms move and why, when they come to expand, they choose to open new establishments in one place rather than in another or instead of simply expanding their existing premises.

This unit concentrates on the second issue of business movement or deliberate choice of a new location rather than on the reasons why particular areas have become associated with certain kinds of firms and activities.

It is important to remember that a decision to relocate or to locate a new part of the enterprise is an investment decision. The firm is incurring costs now in the anticipation that these will enable it to add to its profits in the future. Moreover, the investment is likely to determine the direction of the firm's expenditure and the sources of its profits for a substantial period of time, longer, in fact, than many investment decisions involving the acquisition of new equipment. In practice, of course, many locational decisions are linked to movements into new markets, product sectors or to adopt new developments of technology. In these cases the choice of location is an important part of the total investment. Locational advantages and disadvantages will affect the total package. When we consider the location issue in this light we recognise that account has to be taken of possible future developments and of future risks and uncertainties. Consequently, sites which promise flexibility and the ability to help the firm adapt to changing conditions are likely to be viewed with more favour than sites whose advantages are linked to special features that may well be transitory. For example, a site with ready access to national road, rail and air transport networks is likely to be favoured above another with speedy access only to a rail depot on a line which might be closed in the future.

The main locational influences

We would expect the firm to be influenced by all the main factors that are relevant to the processes of production and distribution.

* **Resource inputs**
  Most of us are aware that these have been important in the past but are rarely significant to modern location in an island as small as Britain. Firms no longer have to locate close to coal, mineral ores, clays, sands or other special resources. Essential inputs can be transported or, often, be created by chemical process. Power is readily available throughout Britain but may still be an issue in other countries.

* **Economic factors of production**
  By these we mean **land** (in its spatial sense), **labour**, **capital**, and the existence of an **enterprise** culture. When firms are investing in new projects, often with new technology, they tend to prefer green-field sites. Not unnaturally, there can be hostility to this in Britain where green fields are already being sacrificed to urban and transport developments at a rate which many find disturbing. This can turn the attention of managers to possibilities in other countries, especially those encouraging rapid industrial development. In Britain, land is a highly regulated factor subject to planning controls and the uncertainties of both national and local political pressures.

  Labour, especially skilled manual labour, is a strong influence on location at local, regional and national levels. Firms have been known to be reluctant to move more than a few miles from existing sites because of their reliance on local pools of skilled, experienced labour. These include married women and retired workers, who form a reserve prepared to work varied and flexible hours according to the changing needs of the firm. Labour is a relatively immobile production factor. Housing, education and the social structure of the family and neighbourhood make moving a disturbing, even traumatic experience once roots have started to become established. The modern, two career family is even less mobile than the old style single career family because movement requires a 'double coincidence of career opportunities'. Transport developments have enlarged the potential employment zone for most people, especially those living in the major conurbations of the midlands and south-east of England but these are now coming under pressure from road congestion. If economic developments require labour to be more mobile within and between countries there will have to be some fundamental adjustments to the social structures of housing, education, child care. Firms may even have to start employing family teams rather than individuals.

Capital is not normally considered to be a major influence within or between countries. Modern finance markets are international and business firms can raise or move finance with considerable freedom in spite of exchange controls. Nevertheless, it is easier to raise the relatively small sums needed by new small business activities in some areas than in others. Where there is a strong tradition of individual business local finance markets still exist. These are supplied from the resources of the successful who are willing to encourage others, and to share in the rewards of their success. Business enterprise can only flourish within a favourable cultural climate. Such a culture needs to accept that the pursuit of wealth can be a creative activity and can lead to a general improvement in living standards provided it is associated with an acceptance of individual social responsibilities and obligations to the community which is the source of that wealth. Business enterprise rarely flourishes in cultures dominated by a State machinery controlled by people dedicated to the appropriation and re-allocation of the wealth and resources of others.

- **Market influences**
The aim of all production is to supply to consumers the goods and services they want and are willing to sacrifice their resources to obtain. The market, therefore, influences location in two ways. It needs to communicate to producers the changing wants, aspirations and attitudes of consumers and it must organise the physical provision of products to the people wanting them. Distance is a barrier to communication and it raises transport costs. It is not, however, an insurmountable barrier nor is it such a strong barrier as closed minds and inflexible, arrogant attitudes. Consequently, it is not really surprising that, in the 1970s and 1980s, Japanese motor vehicle manufacturers were able to produce vehicles more satisfying to British customers and at generally lower prices than could the manufacturers long established in Britain. Nevertheless, in spite of their successes, Japanese manufacturers have recognised the desirability of moving physically closer to their European customers.

Behavioural aspects

Behavioural theory, along the lines drawn by Cyert and March in the 1950s, has made an interesting contribution to understanding business decision-making. It suggests that decision makers:

- seek **satisfactory** levels of achievement in the pursuit of a range of objectives set by the interaction of the various members of the coalition of shareholders, managers, customers and workers which we call the firm and do not seek optimum achievement in the pursuit of a single goal.
- **react to problems** as they arise rather than look for continuous optimum conditions.
- seek the **first acceptable rather than best possible solution to problems**. Search for optimum solutions, in many cases, might change the perception of the problem, e.g. falling demand for a product might really require a major change in product and production method rather than, say, a price reduction or increase in advertising.
- **adapt objectives** in the light of experience and the perceived experiences of other organisations.

In the light of the above it becomes easier to see why firms tend to leave major locational decisions until production or other problems become pressing and then seek the smallest possible adjustment needed to solve the immediate problem. It is often some years after a merger before 'rationalisation' of the different plants takes place. As long as profit objectives of existing plants are met they are frequently left alone even though cost savings could be made by locational reorganisation. Relocation of production then becomes part of a major cost-cutting exercise when economic recession makes reform essential for the firm's survival. Consequently, workers are made redundant in a period when alternative employment is difficult to find, especially as the plants closed tend to be those in areas which traditionally have relatively high rates of unemployment.

It must be remembered that behavioural theory explains what firms actually do and not what they should do in order to achieve higher levels of absolute and allocative efficiency.

The modern multi-establishment organisation

Traditional theories of business location often appear to assume a single establishment organisation or an organisation each of whose establishments can be regarded as independent units. Location is then seen as a compromise between a number of conflicting pressures where, perhaps, the logic of production costs conflicts with the desirability of location close to a large market area.

Today, however, modern communications permit the firm to have different establishments where each is able to exploit locational advantages relevant to its particular function. For example, a senior management team may be located in London close to the centre of political power where links with government and civil service can be cultivated — and the managers remain close to their clubs. Marketing departments can be located either in London which remains the hub of the national transport and communications system or close to a major market area. Research and development can be located in a science park adjacent to a major university to maintain links with current research and tap the talents of suitable research leaders. Actual production can be located in areas of low-cost labour where trade unions do not challenge managerial authority, possibly in a newly industrialising country, while administration can be located in yet another area where there is a supply of suitably skilled, low-cost labour.

The cost benefits of such a fragmented multi-locational structure are clear but there are equally evident dangers from fragmentation. Technical communications may be advanced but human communications can become almost non-existent with virtual warfare breaking out between different functional sectors of the organisation. Interaction between design, production and marketing, essential for any firm seeking to survive in today's competitive international markets, can almost disappear with damaging consequences for the firm's market performance. There is no ideal locational structure for any firm operating in dynamic, changing markets. Managers have to be aware of and seek to solve the problems arising from any given structure.

Governments and business location

Government concerns with business location

Governments become interested in business location when regional economic inequalities threaten to become embarrassing political issues. In Britain the rise of the Scottish and Welsh nationalist parties and the survival of the Liberal party in south-west England have been associated with the failure of these regions to keep pace with economic growth elsewhere in the country.

Most of the unemployment black spots of the 1960s were very much the same as those identified in the influential report on regional unemployment by Lord Beveridge in the early 1940s. These were areas which had suffered from the decline of the old heavy coal, steel and metal industries and the drift away from the north and west towards the new industries and service occupations of the south and east. A certain amount of success had been achieved during the Second World War in moving factories away from the attentions of German bombers into new areas and this appeared to suggest that 'footloose' industries, i.e. industries not dependent on particular localities for basic sources of power or materials, could be encouraged to develop in the regions and help to spread the prosperity which was then being enjoyed by the south-east and midlands of England. Consequently, almost the whole thrust of British regional policy from around 1963 to 1980 was directed towards 'moving work to the workers'. It was based on a 'stick and carrot' approach. The stick was represented by planning controls, especially the notorious Industrial Development Certificates (IDCs) which made it extremely difficult to build or extend business premises against the wishes of the government of the day. The carrot consisted of financial incentives. These tended to swing between outright grants towards capital investment for approved industries in selected areas and allowances against taxation for approved categories of investment spending.

Problems of regional assistance

The massive regional assistance of the 1960s and 1970s achieved some reduction in the gap between the prosperous and the relatively depressed areas but increasingly the cost had to be questioned. By 1979 the expenditure for each new job created was escalating and there was some doubt as to how many genuinely new jobs were, in fact, being created. The list of doubtful aspects of the policies was growing and included:

- **Encouragement of branch development**
  Large firms were better able than small firms to secure regional finance and used it to locate branches in assisted areas. If these only remained viable as long as incentives were available they did not survive when help was removed.

- **Aid was spent overseas**
  Aid was usually made available for spending on capital investment and much of the equipment purchased was imported. Money intended to generate increased activity in the regions actually went to other countries.

- **Aid went to foreign as well as British firms**
  This reduced the cost of entry to British markets and helped to increase foreign competition.

- **New jobs in assisted areas frequently displaced workers elsewhere**
  Firms used the financial incentives to restructure their organisations and many of the jobs created in the assisted areas replaced a greater number of jobs lost in other regions.

- **Assistance tended to be concentrated on manufacturing**
  For most of the period of large-scale regional aid to the service sector was neglected and most help went to manufacturing, especially to the older,

declining industries most likely to be located in the areas of high unemployment. The incentives probably helped many firms to survive and delayed the reorganisation that was needed to ensure the manufacturing sector's survival in the changing world economy.

- **Assisted areas were often too wide**
  Only in the late 1970s was there general recognition that 'depressed regions' could include areas of prosperity while 'prosperous regions' could include areas of decline with problems more serious than those suffered in the assisted areas.

- **Grey areas were created**
  Incentives introduced in attempts to persuade firms in, say, the south-east to relocate in the north-west were more likely to encourage movement from localities on the fringes of the assisted areas. This created a wider area of decline and as the boundaries of assisted areas were expanded new grey areas developed. The logical result would eventually have been to make the whole country an assisted area!

Modifications to regional policies

In the light of the distortions produced by large-scale regional assistance a growing number of economists and politicians became convinced that the **economic** case for government intervention was weak. Most, however, were ready to concede that some measures were necessary to mitigate the social and political problems arising from economic decline. The main developments in the 1980s were:

- **Encouragement of areas with growth potential**
  A series of enterprise zones were created. Although these did not receive direct financial assistance from central government, local authorities were encouraged to give relief from local taxes and some planning restrictions were relaxed.

- **Replacement of automatic aid by selective assistance**
  To qualify for financial help firms had to demonstrate that projects were creating genuine new employment. Attempts were made to encourage growth and innovation through a system of regional enterprise grants. Firms were also encouraged to obtain professional assistance in planning new development in an effort to ensure that assisted projects had a viable long term future.

- **Aiming aid at specific targets**
  One of the main targets was to try and assist re-development in the inner cities whose condition in many countries was emerging as a major social problem of the late twentieth century. Reluctant simply to throw money at this long-standing issue the government in Britain sought to encourage private investment.

- **Co-operation with the European Community**
  One of the bargains made with other members of the European Community was that the UK should benefit from the creation of a Regional Fund. In many ways this was a device to enable the UK to reduce the net cost of Community membership. Many Community assisted schemes have been arranged but channelling aid through the Community has been criticised on the grounds that it is too heavily biased towards transport developments that are not always in the best interests of the regions and not enough attention is paid to the stimulation of genuine local business enterprise.

- **Regional development corporations**
  These have been established to try and encourage the entry of private capital to regions. Their performance has been mixed. Relationships with local authorities have sometimes been less than friendly and some have been criticised for failure to understand local needs.

It is interesting and, for supporters of market economics, encouraging to note that a significant amount of movement of firms from the south-east to the north and midlands has started to take place to the extent that reference is now made to the reversal of the north-south drift, a reversal that a decade and a half of expensive regional incentives failed to accomplish. The more competitive economic climate has convinced a growing number of firms that the benefits of locating in the south-east are not sufficient to justify their expense.

Discussion and revision questions

- What sector of industry or commerce predominates in your local area or, if you live in a mainly rural area, your nearest urban locality? Suggest reasons why this predominance has developed? Do the factors that caused it still remain? If not, why has the pattern of activity outlived its causes?

- Outline the history of one manufacturing company that has been in existence for at least twenty years. Identify any major locational or re-locational choices that the company had to make during its history. Try to establish the reasons for the locational choices that were made, identifying any pressure that might have been applied by government. Taking full advantage of the benefit of hindsight assess whether the company made the correct locational choices.

- In the light of reports made for either or both the above questions and in the light of your own further reading and investigations discuss the extent to which the modern manufacturing company is 'footloose' in the sense of being free to choose any location within the United Kingdom in accordance with its own assessment of costs and benefits.

- What evidence can you find that the north-south drift of industry and commerce in the United Kingdom that has prevailed for most of this century is being reversed? How would you account for such a reversal?

- The British government's regional policies in the 1960s and 1970s appear to have been based on the belief that it was both possible and desirable to spread economic growth more evenly between the regions of the United Kingdom. How did the government seek to achieve this objective and with what success?

- The argument has often been advanced that improved communications, especially roads, are necessary for regional development because these encourage exports. More recently the counter argument has been heard suggesting that regions suffer from improved roads because these make it easier for imports to compete with local production and for national multiples to dominate trade and distribution. Discuss this conflicting view of the desirability of road development. What additional factors do you think should be taken into account when assessing the desirability of such development?

- What part, if any, should a modern government play in seeking to encourage higher rates of economic growth and rising living standards in the less prosperous regions of a country?

Multiple Choice Questions

The following key applies to the next five questions

A   1 only is correct
B   1 and 2 only are correct
C   1, 2 and 3 are correct
D   2 and 3 only are correct

- If a region of the United Kingdom displays the following characteristics it is likely to be suffering from a higher than average level of unemployment

  1   A high concentration of heavy manufacturing industry
  2   A high proportion of school leavers continue in full-time education
  3   A high proportion of its workforce classified as self-employed

- The following represent obstacles to labour mobility.

  1   A high proportion of households are purchasing their own homes through mortgages

2   In a growing number of families both partners are pursuing their own careers

3   The government is trying to replace company-based pensions by individually-arranged pensions

- The following tend to reduce the value of the regional multiple and the consequent benefits of government financial aid to the regions

    1   Domination of the retail trade by the large national multiples
    2   Acquisition of local manufacturing companies by major multinational companies
    3   The use of imported basic materials and manufacturing equipment

- In Britain, enterprise zones are areas selected by the government

    1   on the grounds of their very high rates of unemployment
    2   in the belief that they have the potential for economic growth
    3   to receive benefits from reductions in physical controls and local taxation

- State whether the following statements are true (T), false (F) or value judgements (V)

    a   Grey areas of relatively high unemployment tend to develop alongside areas receiving special financial assistance

    b   A high marginal propensity to import tends to increase the value of the regional multiplier

    c   People living in a region have their living standards raised when it becomes more accessible to other regions following the building of a motorway

    d   To reduce regional inequalities it is necessary to ensure that wage levels are the same in all regions

    e   Green Belt and other planning controls over land use are necessary to ensure that house prices are kept within the means of people living in areas of high unemployment

14

The State as producer

Topic summary

The case for public enterprise

Social and political objectives

Markets in the private sector reflect the desires of the people in that market. If those desires conflict with the ethical or moral beliefs of the leaders of the community then the leaders will seek to use the political machinery of the State to impose restrictions on the market and/or to replace or supplement the market place with the State provision of those goods or services they believe to be desirable.

Examples in the United Kingdom of restrictions imposed on a market include the attempt to control the use of addictive drugs and controls over certain breeds of dogs. Examples of the provision of goods or services not provided adequately by the private sector have included the building of roads, the supply of sewerage services and of piped water and the introduction of compulsory education for all children up to specified ages. Most of the these services were originally provided in the face of widespread opposition. Even philosophers expounding liberal views have generally acknowledged that there may have to be a degree of compulsion in the provision of **public goods** in the public interest. By public good is meant those goods or services which, by their nature, provide benefits for the community as a whole. For example, if reforms in sewerage disposal help to eradicate dangerous, infectious diseases then everyone gains from the reduction in risk to health. Similarly, if a local authority insists on preserving a park in an urban area which the majority of people might wish to be used for housing or business development, everyone gains from the resulting improvement in the quality of the air breathed in the area.

Limitations of the private sector

The community might agree that some services which people are willing to pay for and which could be supplied at a high standard for some sections ought to be available at the same standard for all. This can only be achieved by spreading the burden of provision over the whole of the community through taxation. The only way of ensuring that everyone bears the burden allocated by the State is for the State to use its authority and to take some part in the process of supply. It is on this basis that many social, transport and communication services are provided for rural, even remote areas, at standards comparable with those provided to the heavily populated cities.

Natural monopolies

Certain services can only be provided by a single organisation in any given area. It would not be practicable to allow each household to choose from a range of suppliers for water, electricity, sewerage or even telephones (competitors to British Telecom have to use British Telecom's line network). It is not acceptable to allow one privately-owned organisation to exploit the opportunities for making profits provided by a monopoly position so the State must exercise some degree of control on behalf of the community. It can be argued that because controls tend to inhibit enterprise it is better for the State itself to own and direct the natural monopoly.

The boundaries between public and private sectors

It is difficult to refute the argument that the State itself has to organise and supply some public goods. The most fervent supporter of free markets would accept State provision of external defence and the preservation of internal order and most would argue that the State had a duty to preserve sound money and finance — which suggests some control over the banking system. There is, however, remarkably little agreement on where the lines should be drawn between regulation by the State and supply by the State or between State involvement at all and non-intervention in the workings of the market. There is no international uniformity of practice. Different countries adopt different models of State involvement and draw the dividing line between public and private sectors in very different places. This diversity can be seen clearly in the different models of health care provision. The community in Britain appears to react fiercely to any suspected threat to the provision of a 'free' national health service though few have any clear idea how that service is actually organised and directed. In contrast, the community in France regards the idea of a 'free' health service with some disbelief but accepts the concept of compulsory health insurance and financial support from the State both in the provision of health care and in subsidising the cost of illness to the individual. The two different systems appear to produce roughly comparable standards of total care. There are similar international differences in the organisation and control of most other essential public services.

Problems of public ownership and control

There was a general assumption through the 1950s and 1960s that State control over a service implied the establishment of an organisation, usually some kind of public corporation, to provide that service under the authority of statute and subject to the general, if distant, supervision of Parliament.

By the end of the 1970s it had become apparent that this pattern was producing two distinct though related problems.

- **Growing costs**
  The public sector as a whole was absorbing a rising proportion of national economic resources and was threatening to become a crippling burden on the rest of the economy. In 1979 the combined factor incomes of the three divisions of the public sector (public corporations, central, and local government) amounted to over 27% of gross domestic product, measured by income. Of this nearly 17% was accounted for by central and local government. By the same measures in 1989 the total of the three divisions had been cut to around 20% of gross domestic product with under 16% accounted for by central and local government. In 1979 over 29% of the workforce in employment was employed in the public sector, over 21% being employed by central and local government. In 1989 this proportion had fallen to under 24.5%, with over 19.5% employed by central and local government.

- **Declining efficiency**
  While costs were rising public satisfaction with the services provided by the public sector was falling. Long hospital waiting lists, rising crime rates, huge financial losses from several nationalised industries, inefficient rail services were all causing concern and Mr Callaghan was the first prime minister to comment publicly on growing public anxiety at the apparent failings of the educational system.

The underlying problem seemed to be that public services operated nominally for the benefit of the community, lacked clear objectives and control and, in practice, were being operated in the interests of the workers in those services. To many outside observers it seemed that organisational objectives were replaced by the untested theories of self-perpetuating 'experts' and ideals of public service were replaced by trade union imposed restrictions designed to minimise the work effort of employees. There was a general impression that the public sector lacked both management and control.

Causes of the problems

Any examination of the public sector in general and the nationalised industries in particular is likely to draw attention to a number of widely recognised issues of which some of the most significant are the following:

* **Political interference**
When the nationalised industries had been established one of the prime
instigators of State ownership, Herbert, later Lord, Morrison stated his
belief that the new public corporations would be able to combine the best
of both worlds — the independence of the private sector limited company
combined with the public accountability of the public services. At the time
this seemed a reasonable aim since there was a long tradition in the United
Kingdom that major public services could enjoy a considerable degree of
independence from the government of the day. The British Broadcasting
Corporation under Lord Reith, had jealously guarded its freedom from
government control and the education and health service also enjoyed a
very large measure of independence. Schools had successfully resisted
domination by HMIs for example. By 1979 attitudes were changing.

It was probably inevitable that the growth in importance of almost all
parts of the public sector and the sheer quantity of resources they
employed should bring increasing threats to independence. However,
while no one doubted the reality of political intervention from succes-
sive governments the myth that governments could not, and, therefore,
did not interfere continued. Ministers could not be questioned about the
performance of nationalised industries or even about some of their
stranger managerial decisions because, constitutionally they had no
responsibility for these. The exercise of power without responsibility led
to the destruction of managerial morale. Very few people of genuine
ability could be found to head nationalised industries and those who did
soon found themselves in conflict with their political masters. As public
sector management deteriorated in quality, public sector performance
sank lower and the pressure for government intervention became
greater — even though hidden intervention was one of the reasons for
this deterioration. It has to be recognised that intervention was not
always directed towards increasing efficiency. Governments also intervened to support whatever political or economic objectives they happened to be pursuing. This was clearly apparent in the days of prices and
incomes controls when the public sector was always expected to set the
example of restraint even though this distorted their pay structures and
led to further problems of managerial and technical efficiency.

* **Financial constraints**
Because of the growing weight of the public sector, governments sought
to limit its financial demands. Unfortunately public sector organisations,
including nationalised industries, can only obtain finance from revenue
and from taxation via the Treasury. Attempts to limit calls on the Treasury
put pressure on the organisations to raise revenue and obtaining Treasury
finance requires political rather than financial skills. Nationalised industries and the spending departments of the government were dependent on
the political skills of their ministers to obtain finance and this, of course,
gave further powers to the ministers. Constant warfare between a
Treasury trying to limit spending on all sides and departments and

organisations trying to obtain money is not the best atmosphere in which to make rational financial decisions. Public sector managers measured their success by their skills in acquiring money from their political masters regardless of the effectiveness of their spending. All the traditional safeguards to ensure responsible attitudes to finance seemed to be stood on their head. Increasingly complex systems of budgetary control became barriers to be overcome by managers determined to secure budgets larger than their rivals and to ensure that these budgets were overspent; success being associated with ability to spend.

- **Further problems of public utilities**
  Any public utility providing a service regarded by the community as essential, faces the problem that it has to have capacity to meet **maximum** and not just average demand. An electricity generating company must be able to generate enough electricity to meet demand on the coldest winter day, a commuter transport link has to cope with the twice daily rush hours, even a local education service has to provide enough primary school places to meet the demand of new housing estates full of young families. As these estates and the families in them grow older and the proportion of children of primary school age declines the school buildings remain — and closures tend to provoke fierce local resistance.

A utility facing this problem cannot set output at its most efficient level. This has a number of implications including the inability to make full use of the resources it is employing and a problem in pricing. The difficulty is illustrated in Figure 14.1.

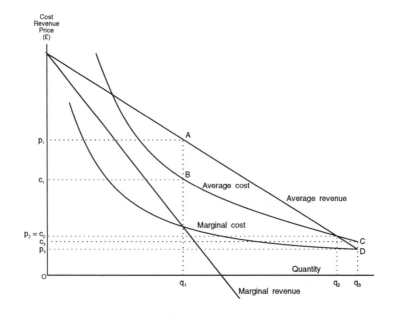

Figure 14.1

Here the utility is assumed to have a monopoly over a particular service and faces the market demand curve which equals its average revenue curve. Because it must have sufficient capacity to meet peak demand it is unable to reach the bottom of its average cost curve and, therefore, its marginal cost curve remains below average cost.

Suppose the utility seeks to maximise profits. To do so it produces at output level Oq_1 where the market clearing price is Op_1 and the average cost Oc_1. Here it makes large profits (the rectangle p_1ABc_1) but has large unused resources and a large part of the potential demand is choked off by price.

Suppose, on the other hand it adopts a welfare-maximising objective where price equals marginal cost, i.e. where the cost of producing the last unit of output equals the value of that unit to the last or marginal buyer. To do this it produces at quantity level Oq_3 and charges price Op_3 which is lower than average cost at Oc_3. Consequently the organisation suffers a financial loss represented by the rectangle c_3CDp_3.

A possible solution might appear to be to set price on some kind of cost-plus basis, i.e. sufficiently above average cost, c_2 (the break-even point where average cost equals average revenue) to provide the desired level of profit. If the organisation does this, it develops a cost-plus mentality where it believes that any cost can be recovered simply by adding it to price. Unions believe that there is no check on wages because price can always be adjusted and so on. The result is the steady increase in costs. The average cost curve rises and price climbs up the demand (average revenue) curve with a consequent reduction in quantity of output and increasing market hostility.

Clearly there is no ideal single price. Recognising this, some utilities, including British Rail, have resorted to price discrimination and have produced a complex price structure that few passengers really understand and which causes misunderstandings and conflicts between passengers and employees.

Privatisation as a solution

By the mid 1970s there had developed a continuing debate over the future of the public sector with special attention paid to the nationalised industries. By 1979 a growing number of people were coming to the conclusion that the only real answer to the problem of organisations in the public sector was to remove as many as possible from the public sector and place them in the private sector where:

- exposure to competitive markets and the removal of the protection of the State would make them more sensitive to the requirements of their customers and the community and force them to make more efficient use of their resources.

- their problems could be handled as economic, organisational and managerial and not as political issues.
- separate control machinery could be set up to ensure that the organisations performed to standards acceptable to the community.

The government embarked on a programme of privatisation applying this not just to nationalised industries but to an increasing range of public sector activities.

The experience of privatisation

Attractions claimed for privatisation

Some of the most fervent supporters of privatisation seem to assume that it immediately brings all the assumed benefits of operating in competitive markets. They argue that it achieves:

- **Removal of political interference**
  The privatised organisation is freed from control by political ministers and managers are left to pursue profits as the reward for commercial efficiency.

- **Access to capital markets and capital market discipline**
  The privatised organisation can seek finance for investment from the ordinary capital market and will receive finance if the market believes its management to be capable of making satisfactory profits. Profits — the return on capital — will be the means of judging the organisation in the private sector and not skill in political manoeuvring. This financial discipline should make the organisation more efficient in its management of scarce economic resources.

- **Reduction in trade union power**
  Because the organisation is judged on its commercial efficiency, attempts by trade unions to weaken management authority will reduce the attractiveness of the organisation and its ability to expand. A union forcing a company into decline is unlikely to be popular with its members whose jobs depend on expansion and commercial success. Unions cannot rely on government intervention to force management to surrender to union pressures rather than face a politically embarrassing strike or other kind of direct industrial action.

- **Freedom and flexibility in use of resources**
  Organisations in the private sector are not forced to keep to a limited range of activities authorised by Parliament. Managers can pursue any line of commercial advantage provided they fulfil the main functions of the organisation and provided they fulfil their statutory obligations. For example, Associated British Ports has been able to exploit its holdings of land in ways that would have been difficult for a nationalised body. BAA is also seeking to manage its airport assets more vigorously and profitably.

- **Separation of regulation from management of the organisation**
Government-owned and -controlled organisations were assumed to be
capable of operating in the public interest without being subject to
separate regulation. The public interest, however, is capable of many
interpretations. When the water and sewerage authorities were privatised it became clear that the old authorities had tended to concentrate
on keeping costs and charges low. Consequently less attention had been
paid to maintenance of physical assets or to avoiding pollution. After
privatisation an independent regulatory body became responsible for
ensuring that legal minimum standards were maintained even if this
meant that charges had to rise.

Privatisation and the public utilities

Few people, other than those politically committed to command systems
of economic control, would argue against the view that privatisation has
contributed to increased efficiency in relation to organisations producing
private goods and services. In a predominantly market economy their
natural home is in the private sector where organisations must justify
survival by ability to produce to the satisfaction of the market. If they are
unable to remain independent or survive profitably then they give way to
those who can. If Jaguar makes more efficient use of its resources under
the control of Ford then it is possible to argue that the public benefit is
served by a takeover which would have been unlikely had Jaguar remained under government control.

This argument does not apply to the public utility natural monopolies such
as electricity or gas generation and distribution, or even telephone
services at the current level of technological development. There can be no
really significant competition in these cases and the community could not
survive effectively without them. The ultimate discipline in the private
sector is the threat that all jobs in an organisation could disappear. The
community could survive without Jaguar cars. There are plenty of rival
cars available. It could not survive without electricity. If the generating
and distribution companies collapsed they would have to be replaced
immediately and the new organisations would have to employ most of the
specialised and experienced employees of the old organisations.

The disciplines of market competition and possible elimination of jobs do
not exist for the public utility which is also a natural monopoly.

Because of the importance of the utilities to the community no government
can avoid responsibility for them. Where there is responsibility we can
expect the exercise of influence. If this is in total secrecy because officially
the organisations are independent of all government control then the old
problems of political interference remain. Having been driven deeper
underground they may be even greater.

The discipline of the commercial capital market may, perhaps, be more beneficial than the political manipulations of the Treasury but there is the real danger that profit entirely replaces the ideal of community service. As early as 1991 there was some public disquiet over the profits generated by the private telephone and water companies in a period when other commercial organisations were suffering from severe economic depression. The regulatory bodies were supposed to defend the community interest but behavioural theory suggests that these are likely to identify with the professional managers of the organisations they are supposed to regulate as time passes. After all they have to rely on management for their information and are likely to develop greater sympathy for the problems of the managers they are regulating than for those of the public whose interests they were established to defend.

Many of the greatest efficiency gains of the privatised bodies were made before the actual birth of the privatised company. This indicates what can be achieved by publicly owned bodies when led by high quality managers given clear objectives and a large measure of managerial independence.

If privatisation of a public utility is simply a transfer of a public monopoly to a private monopoly then long-term gains for the community are difficult to visualise. Privatisation is not the perfect solution to all the old problems of public sector institutions. Most of these remain and we have to admit that no one has yet devised a generally acknowledged effective solution to the difficulties of State involvement in the provision of goods and services.

Discussion and revision questions

- Discuss the view that, outside the special case of natural monopoly public utilities, there is no case for allowing a State-owned and -controlled organisation to enter a product market as a supplier in competition with privately owned organisations.

- 'Throughout history governments have sought to control transport and communications as means to exert their authority over their peoples. Freedom in modern society depends on ensuring that governments no longer have this control.'

  How far would you agree with this statement? Pay particular attention to the role of the State in the provision and/or regulation of television services.

- 'The safety of the community demands that everyone achieves that level of basic literacy and numeracy needed to enable them to cope with a modern urban technological society but education beyond that level represents an addition to personal capital and wealth that the individual should purchase just as he or she has to purchase any other private benefit.'

'Innovation, economic and social progress from which the whole community benefit are invariably gifts provided by talented and well-educated individuals within the community in whose interest it is to provide the highest possible standard of education to as large a proportion of its members as possible if future generations are to receive dividends from today's investment in human capital.'

Discuss these apparently conflicting views of education and the role of the State in providing 'free' education and examine the extent to which they may be reconciled.

- 'Human life is beyond price and the National Health Service should never be ruled by accountants and their balance sheets.'

  'In a modern high income economy more disease is caused by affluence than by poverty and the penalties of self indulgence should no longer be a charge on the taxes of the whole community.'

  Discuss these apparently conflicting views of health care and the role of the State in providing 'free' health care and examine the extent to which they may be reconciled.

- The fact that such a large proportion of nationalised industries were brought to a state of apparently profitable efficiency before, and as a preparation for, privatisation in the period 1980–91 suggests that these results could have been achieved by a determined government without the necessity of privatisation.

  Discuss this statement.

- Define and give examples of 'natural monopoly public utilities'. Explain why most economists and politicians accept that some degree of State regulation is necessary for these bodies.

  Discuss the view that full State ownership and control of such organisations is preferable to the regulation and control of otherwise independent, shareholder-owned companies.

- Examine the view that many of the severest problems of the old nationalised industries arose from the fact that they were:

  (a) public utilities
  (b) natural monopolies
  (c) very large organisations

  and consequently a technical transfer from the public to the private sector of the economy is unlikely to provide a long-term solution to these problems.

- 'No monopoly is permanent. Advances in technology will eventually bring even the strongest monopoly to an end.' Is privatisation likely to hasten or delay this process?

Multiple choice questions

- The real rate of return on investment is the rate

  A excluding any government subsidy for essential services
  B taking into account the relevant rate of inflation
  C before taking into account changes in the value of physical assets
  D before payment of interest on loans from the government

- A public utility adopting a policy of marginal cost pricing would do so in order to maximise its

  A operating profits
  B revenue from sales
  C output from available resources
  D contribution to economic welfare

- The adoption of a common postal tariff for internal letter post regardless of the length or difficulty of the letter's journey is an example of

  A full cost pricing
  B government subsidy
  C cross subsidisation
  D marginal cost pricing

- One of the consequences of privatising major public utilities such as the electricity and gas boards and water authorities has been the

  A government's loss of all revenue from these utilities
  B setting up of a series of regulatory authorities
  C exposure to the risk of collapse in the face of market competition
  D loss of trade union powers to negotiate for workers employed by the utilities

- It is difficult to use non financial performance targets to compare the efficiency of public utilities in different countries because

  A the conditions of operation are rarely directly comparable
  B they have different profit records
  C they are subject to different tax rates
  D State-owned and -controlled undertakings cannot be compared with shareholder-owned companies

15

The business firm and national economic policies

Topic summary

National economic policies

Policy objectives

Most modern governments of market economies would claim to be pursuing broadly similar economic policies though not all would put them in the same order of priority nor pursue them with equal strength. These policies could normally be summarised as:

- **The pursuit of economic growth**
  Economic growth may be simply defined as the capacity to produce more and better goods and services from the available stock of economic resources both physical and human. It is desired because it makes possible that continued improvement in living standards for the majority of the population which is the principal achievement of the industrial market economies over the past few centuries. Politicians desire it because it enables them to offer more and better public services without having to force people to choose between higher taxes and higher disposable incomes for spending on private goods and services. Economic growth makes it possible to have more candy floss **and** more health services to cure the indigestion produced by candy floss. It might also be seen as the device whereby economists gloss over the unpleasant realities of opportunity cost.

- **Achieving and maintaining full employment**
  Unemployment represents a waste of scarce economic resources and it increases the proportion of the population that is dependent on the activities of the employed for the goods and services they consume. It is also, of course, a social and political problem as a pool of unemployed people provides a breeding ground of discontent and an attraction for the recruiting agents of every possible anti-social and disruptive force.

Not least it is a personal psychological danger for the individuals who are unemployed and their families. Most of us wish to feel wanted by the community and we normally have a desire to do something useful and constructive with our lives. Unemployment can appear to be a total rejection of the individual by the community. It is said that individuals in tribal societies, if rejected by the tribe, simply fade away and die. Long term unemployment is an almost similar kind of banishment by the modern equivalent of the tribe — the community.

It is not possible to eliminate unemployment completely. There will always be **frictional** unemployment, i.e. people out of work for a whole range of reasons such as desire to change jobs, conflict with workmates or supervisors, collapse of the employing firm and so on. There is also likely to be some degree of **structural** unemployment. This is caused when an industry shrinks because its products have become obsolete or replaced by something technologically more advanced or simply no longer desired by the public, or when a particular skilled activity declines because it no longer forms part of a more technologically advanced production process. However, if unemployment from these two causes is roughly balanced by unfilled vacancies in other firms or kinds of work which are expanding or in activities which are being created by new technology, then unemployment is unlikely to be a major problem. Some people may have trouble fitting into the changed production pattern but most will only suffer from short-term lack of work. It is when the numbers unemployed greatly exceed the number of unfilled vacancies that the problems emerge. These are magnified if there is a large rise in the numbers of people who are unemployed for a long period and who have little hope of securing work.

- **Price stability**
  Without a reasonable degree of price stability people lose confidence in money. The essential quality that money must always have is acceptability. People accept it as long as they can equate a given amount of money with a known, predictable amount of goods or services. If they lose confidence in the purchasing power of money they will try to avoid accepting it, preferring a simple barter system for their exchange transactions. When this happens, normal trade becomes more difficult and expensive and its volume decreases. We all become worse off.

- **Balancing accounts with other countries**
  The balance of payments records a country's financial transactions with other countries through trade, lending, capital investment and so on. The **current balance of payments** is made up of the **visibles** balance, i.e. the value of goods imported and exported, and the **invisibles** balance, i.e. the value of trade in services and certain transfers from current income. The current balance indicates the country's trading

success or failure and most countries try to avoid having large and persistent current account deficits. These are usually taken to indicate some degree of economic weakness. Besides current transactions there are also transfers of capital and other money flows, e.g. to acquire business organisations in other countries or for investment.

When a country is suffering a large current account deficit the demand for foreign currency to pay for imports will be greater than the supply of such currencies gained from exports. Unless this imbalance is corrected by other money flows it will lead to a fall in the value of the country's domestic currency in terms of foreign currencies. Such a fall in value will tend to make its imports more expensive and exports less expensive. If, as in the case of the UK, imports make up a significant proportion of basic consumer and industrial purchases, import price rises will cause more general price increases in the domestic economy and lead to demands for wage increases, i.e. they will cause general price inflation. To avoid this, a government may seek to attract foreign money — and prevent its flight out of the country — by offering interest rates that are relatively high compared with those available in other countries. High interest rates also cause problems for households buying homes with mortgages and for business firms using bank finance. It is not difficult to see why most countries seek to promote exports and are suspicious of any big expansion in imports.

- **Avoiding regional inequalities in living standards**
  Our perception of how well off we are is based on the comparisons we make of our living standards with those of others. Large differences in regional prosperity cause resentment and political hostility. They can also lead to the movement out of an area of its young and more enterprising people — making it less likely to recover and more likely to go into further decline. The extent to which this is a problem for solution by governments as opposed to one that corrects itself in time is controversial but governments facing the political consequences of regional hostility do tend to see it as a problem requiring some action.

Governments and economic models

If a government considers it has to act to solve an economic problem it must have some set of beliefs concerning its causes and the effects of measures which are within its powers to take. Its views and actions, therefore, are governed by some model of the behaviour of the economy and the economic forces operating within it. As Keynes himself pointed out, governments which do not recognise this are likely to be operating according to an outdated model of little relevance to contemporary problems. Their actions are unlikely to bring about the results they desire.

At the risk of oversimplification it is possible to identify three major models, or more accurately, three groups of models, which have had considerable influence on governments in the second half of this century. These can be broadly identified as command, monetarist and Keynesian.

- **Command models**
  The common feature of command models is the belief that almost all economic forces can be directed by the organs of the State and that the decisions needed to determine production and distribution can and should be made through the political machinery of the State. Thus the **what, how,** and **for whom** decisions that are basic to any economy become political issues to be decided by political process. The underlying motivation for any command economy is hostility to the individual pursuit of profit and belief that the political process will bring about a more desirable economic and social order than that resulting from the pursuit of self interest.

  Command economies can operate where the political, economic and social objectives are limited, easily understood and widely accepted (or ruthlessly enforced), e.g. restoration of German honour and empire through military might pursued by the National Socialist (Nazi) party in the 1930s, or survival in a hostile environment as in more recent Israeli settlements. They have proved unequal to the tasks of managing complex industrial economies. The political machinery breaks down when faced with the mass of complex and often irreconcilable decisions required to operate a modern production and distribution system. The collapse of the command economies of Eastern Europe in 1990 has shown how difficult it is for political structures to take over the functions of economic markets. Nevertheless, while the full-scale command experiments of Communism are unlikely to be repeated for some considerable time there are still large numbers of people who believe that modified command structures can be constructed to mitigate and perhaps reverse those consequences of markets that are perceived to be socially undesirable.

- **Monetarist/classical models**
  These are motivated by distrust of political manipulation of economic forces and by the belief that unregulated, competitive markets are the best means of achieving production and distribution structures capable of raising general living standards. The term 'neo-classical' is often used to indicate the later return to classical thinking after the dominance of Keynes in the 1950s and 1960s. The neo-classical governments of the 1980s have had to face the dilemma unknown to pre-Keynesian governments that they inherited structures within which government agencies wielded enormous economic power and influence. By 1980 the public sector of the UK accounted for a little under 29% of the gross domestic product and employed slightly over 29% of the workforce in employment. Clearly any attempt to reduce the economic role of government in the face

of the vested interests which such a large proportion implied, would require the exercise of just that power that the classical economists so distrusted. Consequently, governments preaching non-intervention and the virtues of unregulated, competitive markets have intervened vigorously in virtually every aspect of economic and social life.

One consistent belief underlying all monetarist-classical models has been the necessity of preserving 'sound money'. Of all the economic objectives the highest priority is given to controlling inflation. This is seen as a pre-condition for achieving all the other objectives because low economic growth, unemployment, balance of payments deficits and even regional inequalities are all, in varying degrees perceived to be the results of inflation. Inflation is believed to make it impossible for domestic firms to prosper in world competitive markets. Hence they are unable to provide full employment, succeed in export markets or resist imports. The conquest of inflation is seen as the means whereby general economic health can be restored. Ideally inflation would be overcome by a return to genuinely competitive markets but, given contemporary conditions, this process has to be encouraged by government action.

- **Keynesian models**

The underlying motivation of Keynesian models is horror of large-scale unemployment and the belief that governments can and should act to avoid this economic and social tragedy. The need for government action arises because a modern industrial economy seems to be capable of reaching a condition of long-run equilibrium where aggregate supply balances aggregate demand at a level where large numbers of people, seeking and needing work, are unable to find jobs. The opportunity for government action to be effective arises because aggregate supply, and the employment it generates, is thought to respond to aggregate demand. Government expenditure plans are the one element in aggregate demand which can operate independently of the business cycle of boom-depression which otherwise dominates the other domestic elements in demand, household consumption and business investment.

Consumer demand (household consumption) is seen as being directly dependent on income. Government action to stimulate demand through its own spending plans can be strengthened by its powers to influence household disposable incomes through taxation.

The policy instruments of government

The three groups of models, though they start from different assumptions, all lead to the practical reality that a modern government will seek to manipulate the economy. It is necessary, therefore, to recognise the tools or instruments available to governments in their efforts to carry out their policies. We can identify three main sets of instruments: direct controls, budgetary measures and monetary measures.

- **Direct controls**

  Governments can seek to use their legal powers and the coercive machinery of the State to enforce their powers to compel actions or to forbid actions. The greater the influence sought over the economy the greater is likely to be its tendency to use these powers. A command economy seeking to control virtually all economic life will control labour and the movement of labour and forbid almost all economic activities which it does not directly control or which it has not licensed. A mixed economy such as that in the United Kingdom will experience varying degrees of control depending on contemporary economic policies. Since 1960 governments have tried, from time to time, to control prices and incomes but direct controls of this kind over private sector organisations were abandoned in the 1980s. Since then controls have been retained only for reasons of public safety, e.g. the criminalisation of drugs dealing, the licensing of premises where alcohol is sold and the licensing and testing of motor vehicles and their drivers. A future government, more inclined to command style economics, could be tempted to return to direct control experiments such as prices and incomes regulation.

- **Budgetary measures**

  A budget is a financial plan relating to actual and projected expenditure and revenue. Government budgets relate to the expenditure of public sector organisations and to the collection of revenue which is dominated by taxation levied by central and local authorities.

  Public sector expenditure is important not only because it represents a significant part of the domestic economy — around 29% — but also because it has a direct and an indirect influence on important areas of private sector activity. Expenditure on education, for example, affects educational publishing and the industries servicing and maintaining schools and colleges; expenditure on roads and railways affects civil engineering and related industries; and of course the incomes paid by the State as an employer of over 29% of the workforce have a major influence on the level of consumer household spending.

  Taxation is normally classified as either **direct** or **indirect**. Direct taxes are levied directly on income as it is earned or on the holders of wealth or property. Any increase in a direct tax reduces the net disposable income and/or wealth of the taxpayers and consequently reduces their potential expenditure. Since net income is either spent or saved the tax also affects the amount saved.

  Indirect taxes, among which Value Added Tax is a major element, are levied on the producers or suppliers of goods and services at one or more stages in the chain of production and distribution. Import duties, for example, are levied at the point of entry to the country, excise duties at the point of manufacture and value added tax at each stage of transfer between firms during production and distribution including sale to the final buyer. Indirect taxes are thus costs borne, in the first instance, by the producer or supplier and like all other costs, these have to become part of the total cost which has to be paid by the final customer. Unlike other costs, however, indirect taxes are not payments for the use of production factors which have contributed to the process of production. They are payments to the government and have no direct relation to any contribution that the State may have made to production. These taxes thus reduce the value received by the consumer for the price actually paid for their purchase. For every £1 paid for petrol, for example, more than 60p goes to the State as tax rather than to the firms and their workers who extract, refine and distribute it.

- **Monetary measures**
  These relate to the government's power to influence the supply and the price of money and credit. In the United Kingdom the government can direct the policies and actions of the State-owned central bank, the Bank of England, and through the Bank influence the lending of the commercial banks. It can do this in a number of ways and, in the last resort, it can effectively order the banks to adopt or refrain from particular practices using the threat of direct action to reinforce its desires. In practice, in the United Kingdom, it has been found that detailed banking controls either become ineffective in the long run or unduly distort the financial markets. Banks are commercial institutions and when their normal business is disrupted by government they will tend to find ways to circumvent controls and restrictions. In any event, modern business and finance now operate internationally and it is extremely difficult for any one government to impose controls that cannot be evaded. Since 1981, therefore, the British Government, heavily influenced by monetarist-classical economic assumptions, has relied on the price of money, i.e. interest rates, as the main means of controlling the supply of bank credit. There is no longer any pretence that the British Government does not directly control interest rates in the United Kingdom through the Bank of England. From around the mid-1980s the Conservative Government used them as the main instrument of economic policy. A different government, under the influence of a different economic model, would doubtless wish to modify this reliance on interest rates and make greater use of other policy instruments.

Policy instruments and the economic models

You will already have recognised the close link between the economic models adopted by government and its choice of favoured economic instruments. These can now be summarised together with some very basic economic analysis.

- Governments favouring command economic styles must rely heavily on physical controls.
- Governments favouring monetarist-classical economic models will distrust direct, physical controls and the use of budgets for economic management but will rely chiefly on monetary policies. Because it is unwilling to exercise direct control over the commercial banking system the government is most likely to depend on interest rates to control the total level of bank lending and credit creation.
- Governments favouring Keynesian models will believe that they must play an active part in economic management and will be prepared to consider any instrument available but are most likely to give first preference to budgetary policies. If a government believes these have to be reinforced it is likely to turn to prices and incomes controls because of its acceptance of a direct link between income levels and levels of household expenditure. The basic, theoretical foundation of budgetary measures can be illustrated through the familiar Keynesian 45° line diagram. This is shown in Figure 15.1.

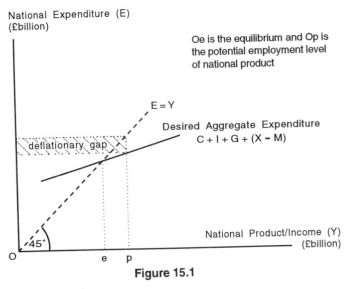

Figure 15.1

This shows the graph of desired or intended aggregate expenditure at various levels of national income and product. Basic macroeconomic theory for any model starts with the concept that there is a circular flow of economic activity whereby the total production of economic organisations is sold to households, other organisations, the government or is exported. Households, organisations or the government also supply the production factors of land, labour and capital to the producers in return for income (rent for land, wages for labour and interest for capital). On the basis of this concept total national product (the total value of goods and services produced) is the same as total factor incomes which must also be the same as total expenditure. Some spending goes on imports so aggregate expenditure usually includes net exports, i.e. exports less imports. It is, of course, always possible that organisations together may produce more goods and services than people wish to buy or that people may try to buy more than is being produced. When this happens the economy will be in disequilibrium but, in the long run, organisations will not produce more than they can sell and people can only buy what is produced. Consequently the national economy will, of its own accord, tend to move towards an equilibrium where aggregate factor incomes = aggregate product = aggregate expenditure. In Figure 15.1 the horizontal axis represents national product and income and the vertical axis represents aggregate expenditure. The dotted 45° line represents the equilibrium levels of expenditure at the equivalent levels of income.

In the basic national income models aggregate expenditure is identified as arising from: the spending of consumers in households (C), the spending of producers on equipment, etc., for use in production, known as capital formation or commonly as investment (I), spending by government (G) and the value of net exports, i.e. the value of exports (X) less the value of imports (M). Thus the desired aggregate expenditure curve is made up of C + I + G + (X − M). Only where this curve intersects the 45° dotted line will the intentions of these forces just match the actual production and the actual possible expenditure at current prices. This is the equilibrium level of national product/income.

One of the important departures of Keynesian models from earlier classical beliefs was that, in the view of Keynes there was no natural force to ensure that this equilibrium level would also be the level where all production factors seeking employment would actually be employed. There could be a long term gap, the deflationary gap, (shaded in Figure 15.1) between the equilibrium level and the potential employment level — the level of production achievable if there were full factor employment. In classical economics such a gap could only be short term because it was believed that market forces would adjust prices and factor prices (i.e. reduce product prices, land rents and wages) until all factors seeking employment were able to find employment at the going rate. Keynes and his followers have argued that such an adjustment would be long and painful and cause massive social and individual misery. To avoid this it was the duty of the government to close or reduce substantially the deflationary gap by raising the desired level of aggregate expenditure. The government could do this by:

- increasing its own spending on public works and services regardless of its revenue from taxes, borrowing if necessary.
- reducing taxes in order to raise the real level of household expenditure.
- encouraging production organisations to increase their capital spending on investment programmes.

All this, of course, implies the use of the national budget not simply to ensure good housekeeping on the part of government, but as an active instrument of economic management to ensure that unemployment is kept to the lowest possible level. It also implies that the government abandons the idea that the budget must be balanced, i.e. that the government can only spend the revenue it receives. Spending is determined by the needs of the economy and if revenue is insufficient then some borrowing must take place.

This kind of policy is also known as demand management and in Keynesian models demand is linked closely to levels of income. Since tax is used to influence the level of spendable income, taxes on income and wealth are more likely to be employed as policy instruments than indirect taxes.

Should the desired level of aggregate spending be greater than is possible from the production possible when all factors are fully employed then there will arise an inflationary gap as illustrated in Figure 15.2.

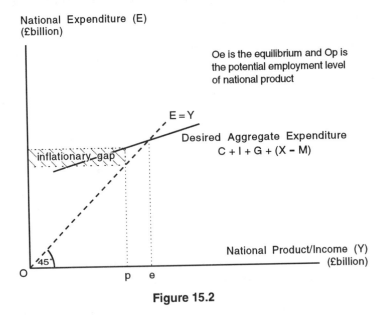

Figure 15.2

Here the potential employment level of national product/income lies below the equilibrium level. Buyers are seeking to buy more than is being produced with the result that the inflationary gap is closed by rising prices and by increased imports. Left to itself an inflationary gap gives rises to rising inflation and a severe current balance of payments deficit. The Keynesian instruments for closing a deflationary gap can be reversed to close an inflationary gap and avoid its painful consequences. Unfortunately government attempts to reduce spending on public works and services and to raise taxes and reduce borrowing are much less popular than the expansionary measures to close a deflationary gap and people will always seek ways to avoid their impact, e.g. by pressing for wage rises and putting intense political pressure on the spending departments of government. It is not surprising that budgetary measures to reduce inflation have been much less effective than those to reduce unemployment.

The impact on business of government policies

The consequences for the economy as a whole of the various models and applications of government policy are outside the scope of this course. Our concern is with the impact on business firms and their reactions. The one certainty is that this impact and reaction rarely accord with government forecasts and expectations, mainly because firms will seek to minimise their effect and try to pursue their own objectives, exploiting any opportunities for advantage that the government's policies may appear to present.

Physical and direct controls

The imposition of direct controls on organisations in a market economy with a long history of business freedom is likely to lead to large-scale evasion and passive resistance. Firms seek ways to observe the letter of the law while evading its spirit, particularly when their impact is seen to destroy the effectiveness of organisations and to make it difficult to achieve their profit objectives. A good example is provided by the various attempts at imposing prices and incomes controls in the 1960s.

- **Price controls**
  These became less and less effective with time. No modern government in a complex economy could possibly police the prices charged for all products and every firm. Evasion is relatively simple by changing the name and packaging of products and making slight changes in composition. As evasion became more skilled and controls more complex the cost of enforcement simply escalated, aggravating the very inflation it was intended to cure. Governments tended to relax controls after a while whereupon prices were raised in anticipation of the next round of controls. Attempts to set minimum price rises were self-defeating as the minimum became the norm which every firm sought to exceed. Price setting became a political game with the government as opponent and with economic reality and customer interest becoming less and less relevant.

- **Wage controls**
  These were perhaps even more harmful and had longer lasting effects. In so far as they operated they tended to reduce wage differentials for skill and responsibility. This was because trade union cooperation was bought by allowing exceptions for the 'low paid'. As skill differentials narrowed

fewer workers thought it worthwhile to make the personal sacrifices of time and money to acquire skills or accept responsibility. As late as the mid 1980s the British economy was still suffering from skill shortages whose origins could be traced to the years of incomes controls in the 1960s.

To overcome the distortions of the labour market caused by wage controls firms started to offer non-monetary rewards to evade the controls. The spread of payments in kind and financial non-wage payments was encouraged by controls and these have continued to cause confusion in labour markets.

Frequent attempts were made to link wage rises to increases in productivity but doing this in a climate of control and wage restraint led to large numbers of phoney deals in some of which officials of the Department of Employment cooperated with managers and union officials to secure forms of words that could be sold as acceptable to the authorities in London. There is also a long lasting legacy of belief that all improvements in productivity must be shared with workers through general wage rises, even though these improvements may be due mainly to capital investment and improved management and may actually involve some increase in labour costs, e.g. in training and the employment of scarce, expensive, specialist labour.

Any form of price or factor price control distorts the market over which it is imposed and the long run effect is frequently to reduce the real value (the potential contribution to economic wealth) of the product or factor while increasing its monetary cost, i.e. the result is usually the exact reverse of the objective of the control.

Monetary controls

Since 1981 the distorting effect of the various direct banking controls through ratios and directives over lending have been widely recognised — though a return to some of the controls have been seriously proposed by a number of recent critics of high interest rates. Consequently monetary control has come to mean control through the price of finance, i.e. interest rates.

High interest rates are intended to operate as a check against high inflation, largely through reducing aggregate demand. They are usually combined with a kind of modified budgetary policy in which government spending is severely restricted and its revenue reduced by tax reductions. The high interest rate is expected to reduce the pressure of household consumption by reducing the supply of money and credit. People can be expected to borrow less if borrowing costs more.

This, of course, reduces the pressure of demand for goods and services on business firms and those firms producing goods and services which are income elastic will suffer most. These will include organisations in the travel trade and the producers and distributors of the more expensive household durable goods such as carpets, furniture and motor vehicles. The effect on demand of high interest rates is greater today than in the 1960s because of the significant increase in the proportion of people buying their homes with mortgages. As interest rates rise large numbers of households find it difficult simply to service their mortgages without commencing any more credit agreements or making purchases that can be delayed. One of the main features of the recession of the early 1990s has been the slump in the housing market. When people are prevented from improving their housing standards or even having to give up homes because of mortgage difficulties there is an associated slump in demand for household equipment, furniture, etc.

Interest rates also have a double effect on business spending on capital investment. Firms increase investment spending in order to increase production capacity. They do this only when they have firm evidence that demand for their goods and services is increasing or is about to increase. If demand for their products is falling or stagnant, firms not only do not increase investment spending, they may reduce it or sell part of the production capacity. They are further discouraged from investing because any increase in the rate of interest raises the cost of capital. At this stage you should revise Unit 9 and make sure you fully grasp the implications for investment, of an increase in interest rates both for the total volume of investment and the life span of acceptable investment projects.

It is the smaller firm operating only in the United Kingdom which is most severely damaged by high interest rates. Large, multinational firms can mitigate their effects in several ways, e.g. by taking more and longer trade credit — especially from their smaller suppliers — by raising funds in other countries where interest rates are lower or by sales of, or closing down, their less profitable subsidiaries to raise cash and reduce borrowings.

For all but the large multinationals interest rates are the most damaging of the policy instruments available to government. There is no doubt that raising interest rates does have a deflationary effect on the economy but the price in terms of increased unemployment and company failures and closures is very high. Some would argue that the price is socially unaccept-able. Moreover, the long-term damage to the economy is also potentially very great and the long-term effect on inflation doubtful. If inflation is believed to be caused by excess demand in relation to available supply then reducing demand is effective only if supply levels are held constant. If the deflationary policies also reduce production then the gap between demand and supply is not being closed as effectively as the policy makers might have hoped. The fundamental inflationary pressures remain to re-emerge as soon as the deflationary pressure is relaxed.

Modern neo-classical governments have sought to avoid reductions in production capacity by encouraging 'the supply side' of the economy. Business and personal taxation was reduced in the belief that lower taxes on profits and incomes would encourage entrepreneurs to develop more business and encourage workers to seek more work. Unfortunately reductions in profits and income taxes only benefit those able to make profits and earn incomes. They do little to assist firms struggling to avoid bankruptcy or workers facing redundancy.

Budgetary measures

Firms in general benefit from budgetary measures intended to increase national product and reduce unemployment. However, if these measures are reversed in an attempt to close an inflationary gap, i.e. if governments seek to cut spending and increase taxes, especially income taxes, to reduce aggregate demand then firms must suffer. There must be some fall in demand resulting from policies specifically designed to reduce demand. In practice the effects are often less predictable and more random than governments expect. Governments find it very difficult to achieve significant reductions in their spending. They conceal this by referring to reductions in the rate of growth of spending or reductions in 'real' spending, i.e. spending increases by a smaller percentage than the average rate of price inflation. Cuts tend to be attempted in areas believed to be weak politically regardless of economic or social benefit. Sometimes political miscalculations are made and intense political resistance is encountered. Politicians are reluctant to risk the dangers of provoking popular outcries against reductions which, individually may be thought to have little effect on the aggregate.

Increases in income tax are now believed to be self-defeating. Raising the higher rates increases tax 'avoision' (legal avoidance that comes very close and perhaps overlaps illegal evasion). It becomes worthwhile to employ tax consultants and a large tax avoidance industry is created with substantial amounts of capital flowing out of the country. In a modern economy it is impossible to prevent finance from leaving a country however harsh the restrictions. If standard or lower rates are increased there are social objections and workers and employers combine to mitigate the effects on net spendable income. There is a rise in untaxed payments in kind or 'expenses' and workers press for increased pay to make good the increased tax. Inland revenue authorities try to tighten the tax net and the tax system becomes increasingly complicated to the satisfaction of tax accountants and at the cost of diverting scarce human resources to unproductive arguments about the distribution and allocation of wealth and away from producing the real wealth of those goods and services that the community actually wants.

Living with economic management by governments

All the usual policy instruments of government have been found to have serious flaws and frequently appear to aggravate the very problems they were introduced to solve. For their part business organisations have to suffer the sudden and not always predictable swings in government policies that can severely disrupt the calculations on which long term investment plans have been based. Because of the serious consequences of failing to predict shifts in government policy firms tend to take evasive action. One way to avoid being trapped by high interest rates is not to borrow and this usually means not investing and not innovating — a sure recipe for stagnant, uncompetitive firms and the economy.

Unfortunately politicians rarely seem to be deterred by their own policy failures or evidence that similar policies failed in the past. There always seems to be some reason why it will be different next time. In the foreseeable future political hazards appear certain to be added to market changes to ensure that business managers operate under conditions of uncertainty. To some extent, however, this can be reduced if managers understand the economic models adopted by the political decision makers and the nature and effects of the policies they are likely to adopt.

Influence of the European Community

Firms now have to take account not only the policy trends of the domestic government and its advisers but also policies of the European Community which is having a growing influence on business law and practice.

Like any political authority the European Commission will constantly seek to increase its power and influence and the amount of finance it controls. As late as 1991 EC finances were still hopelessly distorted by the Community's obsession with the Common Agricultural Policy (CAP). This is shown in Figure 15.3.

Well over half of all Community expenditure is devoted to agricultural price support with the result that farm production is heavily under the influence of CAP and European agriculture becomes more and more isolated from world markets. The dangers for individual farmers when eventually they have to face economic reality are clear.

The main areas of EC influence on industry relate to competition and consumer protection policies and to persistent attempts to impose well-eaning social provisions on business organisations. The contradictions of trying to make firms operate in competitive product markets while making factor, especially labour, markets more controlled and less competitive seem not to concern the members of the European Commission. If the result is to make European firms less competitive in world markets in the face of non-EC producers the apparent response seems likely to be to

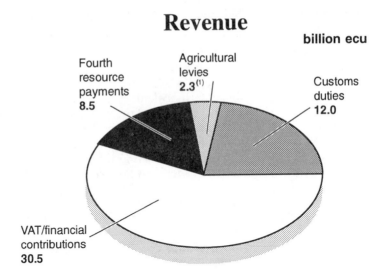

Revenue
billion ecu

Fourth resource payments
8.5

Agricultural levies
2.3(1)

Customs duties
12.0

VAT/financial contributions
30.5

(1)Also includes levies on sugar and isoglucose

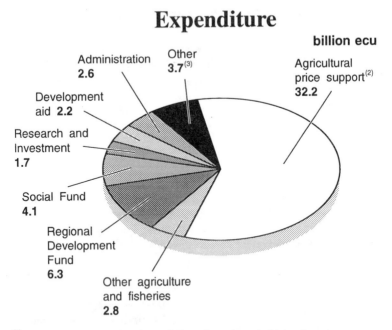

Expenditure
billion ecu

Administration
2.6

Other
3.7(3)

Agricultural price support(2)
32.2

Development aid **2.2**

Research and Investment
1.7

Social Fund
4.1

Regional Development Fund
6.3

Other agriculture and fisheries
2.8

(2)Includes allowance for depreciation of produce held in storage
(3)Includes 1 billion ecu monetary reserve to allow for effects of exchange rate fluctuations between the ecu and the US dollar

Figure 15.3 Note the huge difference between agriculture as a source of revenue and as a cause of expenditure.

resort to increased trade protection. The implications of this trend are disturbing for anyone hoping to see increasing world trade and rising world living standards.

Currently only very large firms need concern themselves with EC competition policies. The Commission only becomes involved when a proposed merger has a large and significant 'European dimension'. The Community's concerns with consumer protection occasionally invite ridicule with some apparent obsessions with the names of products but this is probably unfair to some important work in improving product labelling and in the investigation of the more dubious manufactured food products — including the UK sausage.

Community social policies have some quite important results for firms in relation to employment law and practice. Generally the Community is in favour of equality of treatment and the discouragement of discrimination against groups which in the past have been underprivileged. It has had an impact on British equal pay law and practice relating to women workers and has initiated the movement towards equality of pension provisions for men and women — a trend which may eventually benefit men who now often have to wait longer for pensions than women. It is now becoming concerned with the treatment of older workers and is initiating discussion and eventual action designed to encourage more flexible working and retirement arrangements for older workers.

Business managers need to be as aware of these and other Community trends as of political movements in their own countries.

Discussion and revision questions

- Explain and discuss the extent to which the various economic policies of modern governments are irreconcilable.

- How far and why are government economic policies likely to conflict with social policies?

- Contrast the role of governments in the Keynesian and monetarist-classical economic models.

- Discuss the view that Keynesians and monetarists differ more in the priorities given to their policy objectives than in their assumptions regarding the working of the economy.

- Suggest reasons why interest rates appear to have featured much more in government economic policy and in the public's reaction to that policy since the mid 1980s.

- The main reason why taxation exists is to provide finance for the government. However, in the second half of the 20th century taxation has been used by governments as an instrument for pursuing their economic policy objectives. Discuss the reasons for this change in attitudes to taxation.

- During the 1980s the proportion of indirect taxes in total taxation rose while that of direct taxes fell. Suggest reasons for this shift.

- Why are Keynesian economic policies thought to be much better at coping with high unemployment than with high inflation?

- Employers might be expected to welcome wage controls but in practice during periods when such controls were in force many employers co-operated with their workers to find ways to circumvent them. Suggest reasons for this co-operation.

- Why are high interest rates believed to be damaging to industry? How is it that a government forces up interest rates in spite of this damage?

- 'The government has very wide powers. If it wished to do so it could simply make it illegal to raise any prices.' Could it? If it could, why doesn't it do so?

- How are business firms affected by an increase in income tax?

- Discuss the view that business throughout the community should be subject to the same laws and regulations.

- Use a computer spreadsheet to set up a model wage structure for a small community using simple figures. Use your spreadsheet to estimate the effects on that wage structure of establishing a minimum wage set at two thirds of the weighted average wage in the community. Discuss your findings and the implications for the community of adopting such a minimum wage policy.

Multiple Choice Questions

The following key applies to the next five questions

    A   1 only is correct
    B   1 and 2 only are correct
    C   1, 2 and 3 are correct
    D   2 and 3 only are correct

- The Keynesian and monetarist models of the economy are similar in that they assume
  1 inflation to be the result of excess aggregate demand over available aggregate supply
  2 unemployment to be the result of insufficient aggregate demand in relation to potential aggregate supply
  3 income tax to be the most effective way to reduce aggregate demand

- High interest rates damage many business firms because they
  1 penalise firms that have borrowed funds for expansion
  2 raise the costs and uncertainties of capital investment
  3 encourage workers to seek higher wage increases

- A reduction in government spending affects firms by
  1 reducing the aggregate level of demand for goods and services
  2 increasing the demand for goods produced in the private sector
  3 reducing the production costs of goods produced in the private sector

- An increase in the standard rate of income tax affects firms by reducing
  1 the aggregate level of demand for goods and services
  2 net wages of workers and consequently the cost of producing goods and services
  3 pressure from workers for wage increases

- An increase in value added tax
  1 has no effect on firms which simply add the tax to prices
  2 increases the revenue available to governments for public sector spending
  3 reduces the benefits obtained by consumers from a given level of spending

- State whether the following statements are true (T), false (F) or value judgements (V)
  a In the Keynesian models unemployment and inflation have different causes whereas in monetarist/classical models unemployment is believed to result largely from inflation.
  b Government imposed wage controls are associated with distortions in labour markets and a growth of non-monetary payments to workers.
  c If it becomes clear that there is a persistent deficit in the current balance of payments firms can expect a fall in the foreign exchange value of the domestic currency and/or an increase in interest rates.
  d A reduction in government spending with tax rates remaining unchanged will inevitably increase the total demand for private sector produced goods and services.
  e An increase in the standard rate of income tax will reduce the net income of workers and enable firms to spend more of their revenue on capital investment.

Index _____